To P(...)

Best wis(...)

Rosemary Fitzherbert Jones
20 June 2015

Oxford's Medical Heritage
THE PEOPLE BEHIND THE NAMES

Rosemary Fitzherbert Jones

Published by Rosemary Fitzherbert Jones

ISBN 978-0-9552725-1-6

Designed, typeset and printed by the Medical Informatics Unit,
NDCLS, RDM, University of Oxford. Tel: 01865 222746

Foreword

Buildings acquire names only from persons of considerable merit. It is sad if those who work every day in such buildings have no idea about how they acquired such names. Oxford hospitals have housed extraordinary people. It is a great initiative of Rosemary Fitzherbert Jones to have produced such a readable account of so many who deserve to be better known to the workforce inhabiting Oxford's hospitals. It should be required reading of medical students and allied health professions in training. Visitors from other countries will benefit and so will many who are cared for on the wards and as outpatients.

There have been few historians of Oxford medicine and over the last few years Rosemary has carefully annotated the notes of one of these, Alastair Robb-Smith. He focused particularly on Sir William Osler in his many publications and Rosemary reminds us about Osler in this book. The Robb-Smith archives are housed at 13 Norham Gardens, North Oxford where Sir William Osler, Sir George Pickering, and Richard Doll once lived as Regius Professors. There one may read longer versions of the works and biographies of many of those written about in this welcome book.

Terence J. Ryan, Emeritus Professor of Dermatology

Introduction

The idea for this book stems from the work I did cataloguing papers connected with Sir William Osler. He was the Regius Professor of Medicine in Oxford from 1905 to 1919 and was one of the greatest physicians of his time. It set me thinking. Wouldn't it be good if clinical medical students could learn about Osler and all the other medical figures whose names they come upon as they move around the different hospitals in Oxford. Then I thought that such a book might be of interest to students in other medical disciplines such as nursing and physiotherapy, to everyone working in the hospitals, to medical alumni, and also to patients and their visitors. Other people interested in medical history and those interested in the history of Oxfordshire will, I hope, enjoy it too.

It seems a shame if people don't know about these medical figures, because so much of our medical practice and knowledge today depends upon the work of those who have gone before. Some have been not only important in medicine in Oxford, but have made contributions of national and international importance. Some of the figures have been immortalised because they were generous benefactors.

The biographies in this book are limited solely to Oxford figures (including some non-medical benefactors) after whom a hospital, a ward, or other department is named. This means, of course, that many figures of equal importance are not included. Within each hospital I have arranged the biographies chronologically so that, to some measure, I can paint a picture of the evolution of medical practice in Oxford and beyond, from the fourteenth century to the present day.

Certain common features emerge. Firstly, perhaps unsurprisingly, the major benefactors have often been childless, making it easier for them to leave their wealth to the medical profession. Secondly, one tends to feel that those doctors who came to eminence did so because they were brilliant men or women and that it all came easily to them. On the contrary, I was struck by how hard they worked. I used to wonder how Sir William Osler accomplished so much, yet he and his wife entertained so many doctors and students at their home in North Oxford. It was known as the 'Open Arms'. In actual fact, it turns out that after dinner Osler would slip away to his study, leaving his wife Grace to look after the guests. Similarly, Hugh Cairns's son told me that his father never wasted a moment. If it was four minutes till dinner, he would use the time to write a quick letter or card.

So many of the figures I have written about command great admiration. If I had to choose one, I think it would be Dame Rosemary Rue. She overcame great personal difficulties and achieved so much. She fought against the discrimination experienced by women doctors at that time and she brought about changes leading to the career opportunities women doctors enjoy today. During her life she suffered from tuberculosis and later poliomyelitis but would not let these misfortunes stand in her way and adapted her career accordingly.

Of the doctors I talked to about their career, I was struck by how generous they were to give of their time to me and how remarkably self-effacing they were. Perhaps this is the sign of true greatness.

RCFJ

Acknowledgements and Thanks

I have many people to thank for their help in the production of this book. First of all, Doctor Peggy Frith and Professor Terence Ryan who have taken an interest in the project from the beginning and have given sound advice. Professor Alastair Buchan, Head of the Medical Science Division and Dean of the Medical School, has given me his support. Sir David Weatherall, Sir Peter Morris, Professor Michael Gelder, Professor Derek Jewell, and Professor John Ledingham have all given generously of their time in talking to me about their life and career.

Jayne Todd, Head of Alumni Relations, Oxford Medical Alumni, has given valuable ideas and contacts. Elizabeth Boardman of the Oxfordshire Health Archives has given me help and provided me with photographs as has Ruth Charity, Arts Coordinator of the Oxford University Hospitals NHS Trust. Doctor John Cairns and Doctor Alexandra Cairns have also been of help. Vivien Thornton-Jones of Bagot and Drake Ward, Sister Marie Craze of the Jane Ashley Centre and Professor Wardman and Christel Turner of the Gray Institute have all been kind and helped me beyond the call of duty. Doctor John Ward has provided information about Sir William Osler, and Roy Overall about May Davidson. Lord Tebbit has kindly taken an interest and supplied photographs. Colin Corlett of Northumberland Tales has been most helpful as have Doctor Stephen Richards and Father Darren McFarland. Viv Wightman of the Radcliffe Guild of Nurses has taken an interest in the project.

Robin Roberts-Gant of the Medical Informatics Unit has been of great help and encouragement in the production of this book.

Last, but not least, I thank my husband Simon for all his help and support during the writing of this book.

Contents

The John Radcliffe Hospital

The Warneford Hospital

The Nuffield Orthopaedic Centre

The Churchill Hospital

Old Road Campus, Churchill Hospital

The John Radcliffe Hospital

Photo: Lanercost Priory where Nicholas Tingewick cared for Edward I

Doctor Nicholas Tingewick (d. *c*.1339)

The Tingewick Society is responsible for putting on the annual medical students' pantomime and raises money for good causes. At the suggestion of Doctor Alastair Robb-Smith, who played a role in the first production, it is named after physician and clergyman Doctor Nicholas Tingewick. He was the first known teacher of medicine in Oxford and was physician to King Edward I. There is a hall and foyer named after him at the John Radcliffe Hospital too. He is sometimes called Nicholas de Tynchwycke which suggests he originated from Tyngewick, a village in Buckinghamshire on the road from Oxford to Cambridge, although there are no records of him there.

We do not know when he was born, but we do know that he became rector of the parish of Broughton in Craven in Yorkshire in December 1292. By this time he had achieved his Oxford MA. As was the custom at the time, whilst holding the living he was granted leave of absence from his benefice to study at university either at home or abroad. In 1296 it seems that he accompanied the Bishop of Winchester abroad. In 1300 he became Rector of Coleshill in Berkshire but got into trouble with the Archbishop of Canterbury on account of 'plurality', holding more than one living at a time. He was, however, still allowed to receive the 'fruits of the church'.

By 1306, Nicholas was physician to King Edward I. We do not know how he came to the notice of the King's household nor how and where he received his medical training. In 1306 the King interceded with the

Pope on Nicholas's behalf so that he was granted the living of Reculver in Kent as well as that of Coleshill.

As far as his career as a doctor is concerned, we do have some information which is surprising so many years after his death. King Edward I praised him enthusiastically. When he wrote to the Pope, he said that Tingewick was the 'best doctor for the King's health'. He said that he owed his recovery from long illness 'next under God to Tingewick'. The King resided at Lanercost Priory in Cumbria for five months during the last year of his life on his quest to subdue the Scots. During this time Nicholas ordered rich ointments and medicines from London to the value of £135, a colossal sum in those days. The King moved on to Carlisle and a little beyond but he was in a sickly state and died in 1307 aged sixty-eight. Tingewick was caring for the King right up to the end, as we know the medicines he obtained included those for embalming the body. The Earl of Lincoln was present at the King's death and was so impressed with Tingewick that he granted him a generous annuity.

Some eighty years after his death, Nicholas's methods had not been forgotten. Thus in a medical compendium written at the end of the fourteenth century, he is mentioned twice. The compendium describes how he made a journey of forty miles to visit a widow who was believed to have a cure for jaundice. He gave her money to teach him the cure. It consisted of sheep's lice crushed with honey and water. (It is interesting that some three hundred and fifty years later, John Radcliffe was prescribing very similar cures, such as the head of a crawfish).

From the early 1320s Tingewick resided in Oxford. As early as 1302 he had purchased a substantial property in Catte Street, known as 'Tingewick's Inn' or 'Corbet Hall'. There is some suggestion that at some stage it became a public house which was patronised by physicians for over four hundred years. It is on the site of what is now the eighteenth-century quadrangle of All Souls College. He also purchased a house in Saint Ebbe's. He granted the houses to the university in 1332, with the provision that he could live in Tingewick's Inn for life. The interest from the benefaction was to pay for two masters to teach Latin in the grammar schools of the university. The study of Latin was very important in the middle ages and had to be mastered before entering the church or any other learned profession. By 1325 Nicholas had obtained his DM and DTh and we know he was an 'external master' of Balliol College.

As far as the teaching of medicine in Oxford is concerned, its growth was gradual like the beginnings of the university itself sometime in the middle of the twelfth century. Right from the early days, Oxford had a tradition of medical knowledge and medical excellence, but it is not clear how soon there was an organised medical curriculum. The men practising medicine in Oxford in the twelfth and early thirteenth centuries may have studied on the continent in one of the famous universities such as Padua rather than in Oxford.

In Oxford, St Bartholomew's Hospital was founded in 1130, followed by St John the Baptist's twenty years later. This hospital had an extensive physick garden and was famed for its treatment of war injuries. With the dawn of the thirteenth century, the area around Catte Street was becoming the medical quarter because it was near to the physick garden and also the apothecaries and spicers in the High Street.

We have evidence of organised teaching of medicine by the beginning of the fourteenth century. There was a 'physick hall' for the study of medicine, probably Tingewick's own house in Catte Street. By this time he was teaching medicine, the first known teacher of medicine in Oxford. The Chancellor's and Proctor's Books for the first half of the fourteenth century tell us something about the medical curriculum at that time. If a student wanted to achieve a licence to teach medicine, then following his Master of Arts degree, he must study medicine for six years. He must give lectures on the theory of medicine based on the works of Hippocrates and Galen. Once licensed he must dispute on forty consecutive days and then lecture for two years in the medical faculty. There was probably some practical training as well. If a student wanted to practise rather than teach medicine, the course was shorter.

The number of medical students in Oxford in the medieval period was always small. It seems that, though Oxford medical men were held in high esteem in the land, being physicians to the King and influencing medical affairs in London, within the University of Oxford itself, the faculty of medicine was not influential. Oxford was a small town (it did not become a city until the sixteenth century) so there was little scope for medical practice, unlike London and Paris for example.

One of Tingewick's pupils was the distinguished John Gaddesden who wrote *Rosa Angelica*, the first English medical book to be printed and an account of medical practice at the time. (A translation of part of it may be seen at the Bodleian Library.) Gaddesden was physician to the Black Prince.

We do not know exactly when Nicholas died nor where he is buried. However, we do know that he was dead by February 1339. We know nothing of his private life, but our knowledge of his career is remarkable for one who lived so long ago, and is an indication of his importance in the history of medicine.

Doctor William Harvey (1578–1657)

The Harvey Teaching Room on Level 7 of the John Radcliffe Hospital is named after William Harvey, famous for his discovery of the circulation of the blood and for establishing physiology as an experimental science. He lived and worked in Oxford during the English Civil War in which he was physician to King Charles I.

William Harvey was born on 1 April 1578 at Folkestone in Kent. His family were yeomen farmers. His father Thomas had two ambitions. Firstly, to raise the social standing of his family so that they became gentlemen. Secondly, to bring about their material wealth. He had seven sons and two daughters, William being the eldest. Thomas was also an alderman and must have been involved in local plans for defence against the Spanish Armada in 1588.

At the age of ten, William went to a grammar school, the King's School in Canterbury. He excelled there, and already showed an interest in the natural world.

In May 1593 he went up to Cambridge to Caius College, where he was soon awarded a scholarship. His study would have included poetry, the classics, physics, and philosophy. He worked hard and graduated BA in 1597. He then began his medical studies in Cambridge. These would be steeped in Galen, the Greek physician who taught and practised in Rome in the second century AD. Galen himself was a follower of Aristotle and his theory of the four humours.

In 1599 Harvey travelled to Padua in Italy, which was a centre of learning, culture, and trade. Galileo was at Padua when Harvey arrived; it was an exciting time and coincided with a renaissance in the study of anatomy. Here Harvey received a practical tuition, learning about remedies in the physick garden, shadowing physicians, and being exposed to dissections. The teaching was very much Aristotelian. Harvey's renowned professor Fabricius himself would have taught Harvey about the valves in the veins (though he misinterpreted their function). Harvey was awarded his degree of MD with great distinction and returned home in 1602.

He then set up practice in London, living in Ludgate. In 1604 he married Elizabeth Browne, daughter of a doctor of physic, who importantly had connections at court, being physician to the newly enthroned James I. Here William began his rise through the ranks of society. In 1605 his mother died, and the rest of the family moved up to London and became wealthy merchants. William and Elizabeth were not blessed with children. After several attempts, Harvey was elected Fellow of the College of Physicians in 1607 and soon became treasurer. He also became a physician at St Bartholomew's Hospital. His connections with the college helped him build up a flourishing private practice, although his reputation as a physician was sometimes questioned.

In 1615, the College of Physicians appointed Harvey Lumleian Lecturer in Anatomy, which was a life appointment. He was required to give a course of lectures annually, including a public dissection. This was held over five days, with lectures in Latin and English. For obvious reasons the course took place in the winter. It was aimed at physicians, surgeons, and barbers.

Some of his notes survive and the lectures reveal much on the evolution of his views on the heart and circulation. Whilst some of the Renaissance anatomists were just beginning to question Galen's views from the second century, remarkably little had changed since his day. His theory was complex, but central to it was the idea that venous blood was manufactured in the liver, and blood moved from the right side of the heart to the left through pores in the interventricular septum and thence to the parts of the body that needed it. It seems that Harvey's contemporaries Vesalius and Columbo had some understanding of the pulmonary circulation. They questioned Galen's theory that the 'transformation' of the blood took place within the heart itself rather than in the lungs.

Harvey also questioned Galen's ideas on the motion of the heart itself. Galen believed that the blood ebbed and flowed through the body slowly in both directions, being used up where needed. Galen thought that the heart expanded and drew blood in from the veins, then the arteries sucked blood out of the heart by their contraction.

Having questioned these Galenic views, Harvey discussed the theory that contraction of the heart ejected blood into the arteries. The heart could be seen as a muscle and its contraction was the active phase, leading to pulsation of the blood through the arteries. Through some unknown connection blood then returned to the heart via the veins. A key observation was that the amount of blood forced out of the heart in an hour greatly exceeded its volume in the whole animal. He argued this was evidence that the blood must constantly move in a circuit. Harvey was aware of the elegance of circles in nature and in society, for example in the world of astronomy. He lighted upon the idea that the blood circulated round the body. The beauty and simplicity of the theory appealed to him and he set out to prove it by experimentation.

Over a period of ten years or so from 1618, Harvey demonstrated his theory of the circulation to fellow doctors and others who were interested, both through his lectures and to select groups in his chambers. He performed many dissections and vivisections on a wide variety of animals, including cold-blooded ones with a slower heartbeat and simpler structure. Indeed his house and garden was a veritable zoo. He had arrangements with butchers and fishermen, and King Charles provided deer from the royal parks. He worked tirelessly every evening. The King took an interest in his work. Harvey performed experiments on his servants, tying ligatures round their arms. He was beginning to develop proof of his theory. He noted the valves in the veins which he termed 'little doors'. His reasoning followed very much Aristotle's way of working and philosophy.

Harvey's theory was finally published under the name *De motu cordis* ('The Movement of the Heart and the Blood in Animals') in 1628. It was published in Frankfurt at a price of a little over six shillings. It was sixty-eight pages long and produced on rather poor quality paper. It is said that there were a lot of errors arising from Harvey's poor handwriting. It falls into two parts. In the first, he points out the flaws in Galen's theory. In the second, he puts forward his theory of the circulation of the blood.

Copies were given to fellows of the Royal College, but many poured scorn on it as being irrelevant to their daily practice and also as being critical of Galen. Some feared that the refutation of the theory of the four humours would damage their practice based on these principles. Yet others ridiculed him. Some Aristotelian natural philosophers criticised Harvey's theory because it did nothing to add to nature's ultimate purpose. It took years for the theory to be well received.

One of the early champions of Harvey's theory was the philosopher Descartes. He very much saw the body as a complex machine with the heart as its centre. He had no time for Galen's vitalist theory of animal spirits or Aristotle's principles. Whilst Harvey originally welcomed Descartes' views, his discovery of the circulation did not preclude in his mind the existence of animal spirits within the blood and heart. Harvey believed that though it was a mechanical pump, the heart regenerated the 'vital heat' of the blood which was full of spirits. He saw the blood as the site of the vegetative and sensitive souls. He saw the Almighty, the divine agent, as essential to the working of the body.

Harvey saw himself as a natural philosopher, very much a seeker after the truth and the purpose of the Divine. Whilst of course his discovery was important, his influence goes far beyond. He was important in the emergence of the new 'science', whereby the natural philosophers became rigorous and impartial observers of natural phenomena. Theories were tested by experiment. We begin to see the divergence between the natural philosophers and the metaphysical poets such as John Donne. Donne made many references to the heart, in an age where it was seen very much as the seat of the soul and 'centre of all affections', but it was the scientists who set about determining the anatomy and physiology of the heart and circulation.

King James I had made Harvey his Physician Extraordinary in 1618. By this time, Harvey was a very wealthy man and began to speculate in property. His father had died in 1623, and he should have died a happy man as his children were renowned and financially comfortable, and he himself was a gentleman with his own coat of arms.

Harvey treated King James I during his final illness in 1625. The new King, Charles I, made a donation to Harvey to thank him for his care of his father. He then made him his Physician-in-Ordinary with the then generous salary of £300 per annum and a healthy pension. Harvey's duties included accompanying the King on visits abroad, prescribing for the royal household, and looking after them during bouts of illness. Harvey got on very well with the King and they shared intellectual interests. On one occasion, the King took Harvey to visit Viscount Montgomery who, following a fall from a horse as a child, had a hole in his side through which his heart could be felt and seen contracting. The King and Harvey exchanged gifts, the King giving Harvey silver plate, and Harvey responding with a gift of marmalade.

Harvey lived in Oxford with King Charles I when the court resided there during the Civil War. He had accompanied Charles to the Battle of Edgehill in October 1642, protecting the King's children under a bush at one stage during the battle. On 29 October 1642 the King and court arrived in Oxford, where Harvey was virtually a prisoner. In December 1642, he incorporated as Doctor of Medicine of Oxford, the same year that Thomas Willis took the degree of MA.

Harvey spent the next four years in Oxford, following his scientific pursuits. We know he mixed with and influenced the other physicians working and performing experiments in Oxford at the time. Indeed, he found them and the students there more receptive to his ideas on the circulation. He left his mark on them, encouraging doctors such as Willis to learn through observation and experiment. In April 1645, Harvey was admitted as Warden of Merton College, but did not hold the post for long as Charles I escaped from Oxford the next year and Oxford surrendered to Fairfax.

Harvey's royalist allegiance had made him unpopular with the

Roundheads who raided his London lodgings and sadly destroyed his belongings, including his scientific records and drafts of his papers. He was classified as a 'delinquent' and forbidden to come within twenty miles of London.

His wife of some forty years died. They had no children. He now had little inclination for his medical practice, and once the republican Roundheads lost their grip on the country, he was able to spend his last days in Bishopsgate in London. Sadly, he suffered greatly from the gout. Sometimes the pain was so severe that he begged a friend to give him sufficient laudanum to end his life. He was a great drinker of the new beverage coffee which was believed to be a cure for gout. He is described as a small man with a pointed snow-white beard and sharp dark eyes, walking stiffly because of his gout. He always carried a dagger.

Harvey had amassed a fortune of some £20,000 during his life. He gave a considerable sum to the College of Physicians to build a library and museum at its original splendid home at Amen Corner which opened in 1653. He also left the college some books and papers, but all were lost in the Great Fire of London in 1666. There was a white marble statue of Harvey there which was also lost. He also left some of his property to the college, stipulating that the rent be used to fund an annual banquet.

In his later years he was somewhat melancholic, though he enjoyed talking and listening to his young followers. He worried about the tumult his theory of circulation had caused—some called him the 'disturber of the quiet of physicians'. He became weary of life. In the summer of 1657, while Cromwell was still Lord Protector and some three years before the Restoration of the Monarchy, Harvey suffered a stroke whilst staying with his brother Eliab. He deteriorated rapidly, and died on the morning of 3 June 1657. He was seventy-nine. His funeral was at Hempstead Church in Essex on 26 June 1657, where two of his nieces were buried in the Harvey Vault. William was buried between them in a lead coffin. However, due to damage of the coffin, his remains were reinterred in a sarcophagus together with his works and an inscription in October 1883, in a ceremony organised by the Royal College of Physicians.

Doctor Thomas Willis (1621–1675)

Ward 7B at the John Radcliffe Hospital is an acute general medical ward named after Thomas Willis. He was Sedleian Professor of Natural Philosophy in Oxford and a neuroanatomist and physician. He is best known to us for describing the 'Circle of Willis', the anastomosis of arteries at the base of the brain.

Willis was born on 27 January 1621 to a farming family in the village of Great Bedwyn in Wiltshire. When he was nine or so the family moved to North Hinksey near Oxford as his mother inherited a small estate there. However, she died in 1631. Thomas walked daily to the school of Edward Sylvester near Carfax in Oxford. At the age of sixteen he matriculated, entering Christ Church as a servitor to a canon (an undergraduate who did menial tasks such as serving meals in exchange for free board and tuition).

He received his BA in 1639 and his MA in 1642 but that summer the Civil War broke out and Oxford became the headquarters of the Royalists. The religious and political turmoil turned Oxford and the university upside down. It probably influenced Willis's decision to read medicine rather than enter the Church. Fevers raged, probably typhus, and Willis's father succumbed in June 1643. His stepmother (who owned a neighbouring farm) died ten days later, so at the age of twenty-one Willis was responsible for running two farms as well as supervising the education of brothers and stepbrothers.

The following year he joined the Earl of Dover's regiment which was stationed in St Clement's, part of the Royalist garrison defending the city of Oxford. The Royalists were defeated in June 1646 and Willis returned to Christ Church, graduating as a Bachelor of Medicine in December. As a Royalist and orthodox Anglican (he allowed divine service to be celebrated in his rooms in Christ Church, against the rules of the Puritans), the climate in Oxford was not favourable for a fledgling doctor seeking to set up in practice. Furthermore, the Civil War had meant that his formal medical training had been brief.

The struggle to build up a practice gave Willis time for his passion of chemistry, which dominated the first phase of his career. He became an active member of the Oxford Club of Natural Philosophers, an influential group making Oxford an important centre for the new discipline of science. Willis saw himself as a follower of Bacon, a seeker of truth by observation and experiment. It was an exciting time, and other important scientific thinkers in Oxford with whom Willis mixed and worked included Robert Boyle, William Petty, Christopher Wren, Richard Lower (see later), and Robert Hooke.

The seventeenth century was a time of great change in the theory and practice of science, beginning to free it at last from the shackles of antiquity. Willis's theory of health and disease was very much a synthesis of the old and the new. Hippocrates' theory of the four humours, enlarged upon by Galen in Rome in the second century AD still held sway at the beginning of the century. Illness was seen as an imbalance of the humours. However, Willis was inspired by the revolutionary sixteenth-century doctor, Paracelsus, and his pupil Van Helmont, although shunning their mystical notions. Willis expanded Paracelsus' three-element theory of matter and believed that there were five chemical principles or particles. Agitation of these particles led to fermentation. Fermentation was equivalent to a humour. He thought, for example, that fermentation within the heart propelled the blood through the arteries. Disease was a result of the morbid state of these ferments. An important advance which coloured Willis's thinking was Harvey's discovery of the circulation of the blood, which had been published in 1628 (see earlier).

Willis was involved in setting up a laboratory at Wadham College where a group carried out chemical experiments. He was an 'iatrochemist' seeking drugs that would cure his patients, analysing material such as blood and urine, and studying combustion. It was an expensive and dirty business, requiring a furnace and assistants and drugs.

In addition, he was developing his interest in anatomy. Dissection was opposed by the Church, although it was permitted on executed criminals. In 1650 the body of Anne Green who had been hanged in Oxford was brought to Petty and Willis at Christ Church for dissection. They found her to be alive and resuscitated her and she went on to bear three children.

All this time he was setting up his practice and during the years 1650–52 he kept a casebook which throws light on his thinking and on medical practice in Commonwealth Oxford. It is a small brown leather volume and it has been translated from the Latin. We know that he shared a horse with another doctor and that he visited towns in Oxfordshire on market days. At that time medical care was provided by the empirics and wise women in the villages, by quacks, and by university medical graduates (of whom there were only a hundred or so in the country). Willis had to compete with all these and it seems that he was often called in as a last resort after others had failed.

His treatment was distinguished by his search for remedies with a rational basis: here was the beginning of the modern scientific study and treatment of disease. The casebook describes fifty cases and is Willis's record of details of the illness, the treatment he prescribed, and also his speculation on the aetiology and pathology of the condition. All in all, Willis's approach was very much a mix of the old and the new, a reluctance to throw aside the old classical ideas despite adopting the new theories. It is an illustration of how changes took place gradually over the decades and how complex the situation was for a doctor in the seventeenth century.

In 1657 Willis married Mary Fell, who was the daughter of a former Dean of Christ Church and Vice Chancellor of the University. She was a staunch Royalist. They had nine children, but sadly five died at a young age, some of them probably of tuberculosis.

In 1658/9 he published his first book *Diatribae Duae Medico-Philosophicae*, which was in two parts: 'De fermentatione' and 'De febribus', reflecting his interests in fermentation described above, and his interest in fevers. He did important work in the latter field, classifying different patterns and causes of fever. He was the first to describe and name puerperal fever.

In 1660, with the restoration of the monarchy, Willis's Royalist views now worked for him, and he was elected Sedleian Professor of Natural Philosophy at Oxford. In addition he was made Doctor of Medicine of the University of Oxford, on the nomination of Charles II.

Medical training in Oxford changed little from medieval times until the sixteenth century which saw the founding of the Royal College of Physicians, the Regius Professorships, and other lectureships. These marked the real beginning of formal medical education. Most learned physicians trained at either Oxford or Cambridge, although many spent some years on the continent. The first seven years (four to the Bachelor of Arts and three to the Master of Arts) were not specific to medicine. Grammar, Rhetoric, and Logic were learned from the classics, particularly Aristotle, and were in Latin and Greek. There followed seven more years, three to the Bachelor of Medicine, after which the student was licensed to practise, then four to the Doctor of Medicine.

During this time, the Regius Professor of Medicine lectured on the Greek physicians Hippocrates (fifth century BC) and Galen (second century AD). In addition, the professor must deliver four lectures on the dissected body of an executed criminal. Medical students must also take part in public disputations and for their doctorate, they must give six lectures on Galen.

Willis's twice-weekly lectures on anatomy, physiology, and pathology were popular. He had to speak slowly and clearly for three quarters of an hour in Latin, allowing for note taking. He must remain for fifteen minutes afterwards to answer questions. Both professor and students could be fined for non-attendance. In the early lectures, Willis carried out the remit of teaching classical medicine, but increasingly, to the dismay of the authorities, he introduced the teaching of the new experimental science. He discussed his own research and that of workers on the continent. Subjects ranged from medico-philosophical topics to practical therapeutics. At last, the relevance of the classical education for treating patients and curing ills was being questioned.

John Locke's notebook with his lecture notes from Willis's lectures survives. The early ones are actually Richard Lower's notes, passed on to Locke who only attended the later series. These are a unique and important insight into seventeenth-century medical teaching. There are some delightful expressions and flights of fancy on Willis's part. For example, he describes animal spirits in the gut that are 'constantly scattered, roaming and, as it were, keeping watch'. When medicinal cordials are imbibed, the animal spirits 'take their new guests by the hand' and take them to the heart and brain.

By now he was developing his second major interest, that of anatomy, especially neuroanatomy and the diseases of the nervous system. He is seen as the founder of clinical neuroscience. In 1664 he published an important work, *Cerebrae Anatomi*, which was a minute study of the structure of the brain as well as the spinal cord, and the peripheral and autonomic nervous systems. It was much more detailed and accurate than any that had gone before. Christopher Wren provided the illustrations and Richard Lower helped with the dissections.

Willis was the first to understand the significance of the 'Circle of Willis', the anastomosis of arteries at the base of the brain. He and Lower injected dye, a mixture of saffron and ink, into one carotid artery of a dog and found that the entire brain was stained. The next step was to tie off all but one of the arteries at the base of the brain. The dog was unaffected and after the procedure, even followed Willis round Oxford as he did his home visits. Furthermore, Willis described a case at autopsy where sclerosis of one carotid artery blocked it completely, and the vertebral artery on the same side was markedly enlarged. The patient had normal mental and neurological function before he died of an unrelated tumour. Here we see that, whilst the anatomy of the Circle of Willis had been noted previously, Willis was the first to demonstrate its physiological importance.

He was the first to classify the cranial nerves since Galen, and it is not so very different from our own classification. He coined the term 'neurology'. Some of his theories were remarkably enlightened. He believed that movement was due to 'animal spirits' which were formed in the cerebrum by distillation from arterial blood. They were then transmitted via the nerves, where they acted as the agents of movement and excited the spirits in the muscles to contract. (If we substitute 'electricity' for 'animal spirits' the theory is not so very different from our own understanding today.) In 1667, Willis published *Pathologiae Cerebri*, again a work of great importance.

Willis now had a successful practice in Oxford, being the best paid physician in the city. With two colleagues he leased consulting rooms in the High Street opposite the Mitre, and developed what amounted to a private hospital. But London seemed to be the place to go, with its scientific thinkers and societies. Furthermore, his patron in Oxford, Gilbert Sheldon, was now Archbishop of Canterbury. He sought Willis's help, both for the people of London recently afflicted by the plague and fire, and for his own medical condition. So Willis moved there in 1667, setting up a practice in Westminster. He read prayers twice daily at his local church, St Martin-in-the-Fields, and gave his services free to the poor. His wife Mary died in 1670, probably of pulmonary tuberculosis, leaving him with the care of four young children. He remarried two years later.

He became a celebrated and wealthy doctor in London and was physician-in-ordinary to King Charles II. He attended the family of the future James II until his plain speaking gave offence. He began to acquire property, including the lease of Ham Court in Surrey, built by William the Conqueror's son. Whilst probably not a 'founder' of the Royal Society, he did attend meetings and continued to associate with the foremost thinkers of the day.

In 1670 Willis published *Affectionum Quae Dicuntur Hystericae et Hypochondriacae* ('Of Diseases which are said to be of the Womb and of the Hypochondria'), which included sections on the blood, muscular action, and on psychology including hypochondriasis and hysteria. Unlike thinking of the time, he believed that the last two originated in the brain.

His 1672 book *De Anima Brutorum* ('Concerning the Soul of Beasts') was considered his most important work, written to occupy his mind while grieving for the loss of his wife. It sought to explain the nature and afflictions of the soul, a question occupying the mind of the new scientific thinkers. Importantly Willis also described in it a number of diseases previously unknown to medical science. He gave a very good clinical description of myasthenia gravis, a condition characterised by fatigue of muscles with activity. Thus he described a woman who temporarily lost the power of speech, as becoming 'mute as a fish'. He described a phenomenon where certain deaf patients' hearing is improved in a noisy environment (paracusis Willisii).

He made a major step forward in correlating clinical observations with his detailed pathological studies, something revived by William Osler some two hundred and fifty years later. He did autopsies on his own patients whenever possible. Noteworthy too is his use of the microscope in this work, again reintroduced by Osler in Canada so many years later.

Towards the end of his life, Willis's interests changed again, and in 1674 and 1675 he published *Pharmaceutice Rationalis*, the first scientific work on pharmacology and one of the major medical works of the seventeenth century. He sought to explain the mechanism of action of the drugs used at the time. As well as being a compilation of the then 'material medica', the recipes are interspersed with clinical observations and with related anatomical and physiological details. Like John Radcliffe, who came after him, we see him beginning to think in systems, disease being due to a specific disorder which may be susceptible to specific remedies. Illness is not merely an imbalance of the humours. This search for a rational pharmacology did not, however, preclude the 'old' treatments of Aristotle, which he continued to use until the end of his life. He coined the term 'mellitus' in diabetes, being the first in Europe to observe that the urine is sweet. Indeed, diabetes mellitus was termed 'Willis's disease'. Willis's accurate case reports are still of value to clinicians today.

His contemporaries respected his skill as a physician and natural philosopher, although one acquaintance described him as 'a plain Man, a Man of no Carriage, little discourse, Complaisance or Society'. He was, however, undoubtedly a hard-working man, devout, courageous, and caring. Even as a boy he was generous, giving his pack lunch to the poor. He travelled great distances to attend the sick. He refused a knighthood.

Willis died of pneumonia in his home in St Martin's Lane on St Martin's Day, 11 November 1675 at the age of fifty-four. He was buried in the north transept of Westminster Abbey following a 'ridiculously sumptuous' funeral costing £470, arranged by his brother-in-law. Willis bequeathed money to his family and servants, and also to ensure the reading of divine service from the Book of Common Prayer at St Martin-in-the-Fields. His practice was taken on by his pupil Richard Lower and thence passed on to John Radcliffe (see later). There is a portrait of Willis in the Lower Reading Room of the Bodleian Library.

Doctor Richard Lower (1631–1691)

Ward 7A at the John Radcliffe Hospital is an acute general medical ward named after Richard Lower. He was an anatomist, physiologist, and physician who is best known for being the first doctor to perform a successful blood transfusion between animals and the first in England to transfuse animal blood into a human. He was pupil then junior partner of Thomas Willis (see earlier), and was an important member of the group of seventeenth-century natural philosophers in Oxford at this exciting time.

Lower was born in about 1631 in the village of Tremere near Bodmin in Cornwall, the son of a gentleman. He was educated at Westminster School in London, then entered Christ Church, Oxford in 1649. He obtained his BA in 1652/3 and his MA in 1655. Willis saw his potential straight away and took him under his wing and trained him well over the coming years. Indeed, although it was to be ten years before Lower obtained his official medical qualification, Willis soon had him visiting his patients as far away as East Anglia. His fees were low compared with Willis's, but he benefitted from Willis's knowledge and wisdom and it led eventually to a lucrative medical practice. Lower became Doctor of Medicine in 1665.

Lower discovered a spring in a village called Astrop near Banbury from which flowed water with supposed healing powers. The sick came from all around to drink of it and wealthy patients stayed in fashionable inns in Oxford. The waters were brought to them and indeed Willis stopped sending his patients to Tunbridge Wells. It was Willis who got the credit for the spring, though Lower did not seem to mind.

Lower's work throughout his life may be divided into three areas. Firstly, his work with Willis on the anatomy of the nervous system. Secondly, his study on the pulmonary circulation in collaboration with Hooke. Finally, his transfusion experiments in which he was assisted by Boyle.

Lower helped Willis with his dissections of the brain and nerves and indeed contributed much to Willis's treatise on the anatomy of the nervous system.

Lower was considered to be the finest dissector in all Europe. He was always dissecting some creature in his rooms in Oxford, sometimes missing Divine Service. In his books, Willis praised him for the sharpness of his knife and of his wit.

Lower's experiments on respiration and circulation began with Willis too. It was known that the veins carried dark blood and the arteries red blood. Willis and Lower sought to answer the question of how the colour of the blood was determined. Harvey's experiments in the early seventeenth century had established the circulation of the blood (see earlier), but Willis believed there was a fermenting fluid in the heart which transformed the blood. Boyle and Hooke questioned this explanation, and over the next decade or so the Oxford group showed in a series of experiments on dogs that the power of the blood came from the air rather than from a chemical reaction in the heart.

In one important experiment, Lower and Hooke showed that when the lungs were exposed to the air, blood sampled from the pulmonary vein which carries blood from the lungs to the heart was already bright red. The conclusion was that a substance in the air was consumed during breathing and it was this that made the blood red, just as the dark blood at the surface of a dish went red. They disproved the theory that the blood turned red through some chemical process or fermentation in the heart. Lower also studied the anatomy and histology of the heart and noted that it was a muscular structure. He proposed that it worked by acting as a pump, thus building on the work of Harvey before him. Lower and Hooke questioned the theory of Willis and those before him since the time of Plato that the heart and lungs were the centre of the human soul and spirit. Willis accepted this correction with good grace and went on to describe the heart as 'a mere muscle consisting of only flesh and tendon'.

Lower's third area of research, that of blood transfusion, is a fascinating story and the transactions of the Royal Society in its early days were full of it. In the late 1650s, Christopher Wren who was one of the Oxford scientists (and was later known as architect of St Paul's Cathedral) began infusing medicines directly into the bloodstream of animals. The results were mixed. Lower and Boyle wondered if a dog could be kept alive by injection of substances instead of by food. They injected a quart of warm milk, but the blood curdled and the dog died.

They then wondered if blood passed from one dog to another might succeed so a tube was fixed from the jugular vein of one to another, but again the dogs died. Lower could see the value of transfusing blood into an animal dying of blood loss. February 1665 brought the first successful transfusion between animals. Lower had devised special instruments that prevented clotting. Realising the difference of pressure between arteries and veins, he and Boyle put a tube into an artery of one dog (the donor) and into the vein of another (the recipient). They bled the recipient nearly to death, then transfused it. The results were dramatic: the dog leapt off the table.

Boyle was keen to pursue the work, but in August 1665 Lower went to his home in Cornwall to look for a bride. He was successful and brought his new wife to Oxford the next year and continued his transfusion experiments.

The excitement now lay in the possibility of transfusing blood into a man. Not only could blood loss be reversed, but more exciting were the possibilities of changing the character or behaviour of a man by injecting blood from another man or from another species. Could the injection of blood from a lamb make a disturbed man meek and mild?

Due caution on the part of the English scientists, unwilling to risk the death of the subject, caused delay and meant that the first human transfusion took place in France. Doctor Jean-Baptiste Denys, who was the eminent physician to Louis XIV, carried out the first fully documented transfusion from animal to man on 15 June 1667. Sheep's blood was injected into a fifteen-year-old boy who survived. There were other successes, but also a number of deaths. Cases where the recipients survived were probably due to only a small amount of sheep's blood being transfused, thus averting a calamitous allergic reaction.

Lower repeated Denys' experiment in London in November 1667 with the first human transfusion in Britain. The Royal Society had set up its own research into the subject and when Lower moved up to London in 1667, he was asked to take over the work. Bedlam would not provide a subject for such an outlandish experiment. In the end, a Cambridge-educated tramp named Arthur Coga was chosen, 'the subject of a harmless form of insanity'. Lower was convinced that a transfusion would cure him. Blood was transfused from a lamb using quills and silver pipes into a vein in Coga's arm. He survived, so much so that he enjoyed a glass of wine and a pipe of tobacco in front of an audience of forty witnesses. However, he spent the guinea Lower gave him on alcohol, so it was concluded with regret that 'the wildness of his mind remained unchanged'. But the experiment had caused a great stir in London and all sorts of speculation about the possibilities. Maybe the old could be made young, the mad be made sane, the shy be made sociable. Pepys wondered what would happen if the blood of a Quaker were given to an archbishop. It is easy to pour scorn on this notion but we have all seen a severely anaemic person 'rejuvenated' by a blood transfusion. However, the number of deaths occurring in France led to the procedure being banned there in 1670, and the Vatican and the British Parliament soon followed suit. Indeed, it was a hundred and fifty years before there were any more attempts at human transfusion.

Lower's move to London in 1667 was a result of the friendship and patronage of Thomas Willis who had just moved to London himself and was building up a lucrative practice. We do not know why, but in 1670 Lower stopped his scientific experiments and concentrated on his medical practice. He never wrote another scientific paper and indeed was expelled from the Royal Society in 1675 for non-payment of dues.

Lower's first publication had been in 1665, a defence of Thomas

Willis's work on fevers. His most important work, however, was a work published in 1669 on the blood and circulation.

Lower lived in various parts of London, finally settling in Covent Garden. He built up a successful practice himself, and on Willis's death in 1675 was considered the most noted physician in London. He was much in demand in court circles, but his political views got him into trouble. In 1678 there was a 'Popish plot' and he espoused the Whig cause because he wrongly believed that this would become the dominant force in English politics. This damaged his reputation and he lost his position in court.

Lower died at home in Covent Garden on 17 January 1691 at the age of fifty-nine or sixty. It was said to be due to a cold caught while putting out a fire in his chamber chimney. His body was transported to Cornwall and he was buried in the church of St Tudy near Bodmin as he had purchased an estate in the parish. He bequeathed money to St Bartholomew's Hospital and to French and Irish Protestant refugees as well as to the poor in Covent Garden and Cornwall.

We have a facsimile of a book, 'Dr. Lower's, and several other eminent physicians receipts: containing the best and safest method for curing most diseases in humane bodies'. It was published posthumously in 1701, written by a 'J.W.' to whom Lower had communicated his receipts shortly before his death. J.W. called him 'the late Famous and Incomparable Physician Dr. Lower'. It was to be of help to those living far from a doctor or unable to afford treatment, and also helped to ensure sensible treatments, as opposed to those of some of the quacks of the time.

The understanding of the diseases and the treatments prescribed are very much those of his master Willis. The remedies contain plant materials, many of them used for centuries by the wise women. Some included steel filings, a tribute to Willis's chemical experiments. Other more surprising ingredients were frogspawn in a gargle for sore throats and 'Compound-water of Earth-worms' for 'Rheumatick Pains'. Doctor Lower prescribed bleeding for the treatment of pleurisy. He prescribed a remedy for vertigo 'to carry the Humour off from the stomach, which fumes up into the Head'. One remedy is to cure excessive sweating arising from the 'vitiated Fermentation of the Blood', a tribute to Willis's theories. His remedy for 'falling sickness' involved taking a concoction three days before the new moon and three days before the full moon.

We may conclude from studying these receipts that medicine was very much in a state of flux at the time Lower and Willis were practising. While a new more rational pharmacy was on the way, the herbal remedies were still the basis of treatment. Bleeding was used, though somewhat sparingly if these remedies are representative of the whole. There is still a mention of the humours. So although Willis and Lower's studies were beginning to increase the understanding of disease, the classical theories had not entirely been abandoned. It was a very complex but very exciting time to be practising medicine.

Doctor John Radcliffe (1652–1714)

If John Radcliffe had married and had children, medicine in Oxford, and indeed Oxford itself, would be quite different. The Radcliffe Camera (part of the Bodleian Library), the Radcliffe Infirmary, and the Radcliffe Observatory were all built with money left by the doctor. His name lives on in the John Radcliffe Hospital and the Radcliffe Science Library.

John Radcliffe was a complex man. He was an eminent and successful physician, acclaimed in one obituary as 'the most eminent physician this England ever produced'. His fortune was amassed through his skill in diagnosis, his common-sense treatment, and the confidence he inspired in his patients. He enjoyed royal patronage and attended wealthy London society. He wrote no learned book, nor made any great discovery. He was a forthright man, who could be rude and insulting to both patients and colleagues but at the same time he could be an entertaining and sociable companion. He tended to drink rather too much, like many of his time. He could be parsimonious, but at other times very generous. He was born during the Commonwealth and for the most part of his life England was going through a period of great religious and political upheaval. This had marked effects on the university and the city of Oxford. Although the teaching of medicine was somewhat mediocre at the time, it was also an exciting time when new scientific methods of observation and experiment were being fostered by men such as Willis and Sydenham. It is said that Radcliffe learned most of his medicine from the eminent Doctor Willis (see earlier).

John Radcliffe was born in December 1652 in Wakefield, Yorkshire. His father was an attorney and Governor of the Wakefield House of Correction. His early promise led his father to send him to Wakefield Grammar School. At the age of only thirteen, in 1666, he went up to University College, Oxford as an exhibitioner. He received his BA in 1669. He had set his heart on medicine and in 1670, in order to fund his studies, accepted a Yorkshire Fellowship at Lincoln College, where he lectured in logic and philosophy. He graduated as a Bachelor of Medicine in 1675 and began to practise in Oxford. He soon made his name due to the success of his unorthodox treatment of patients during a smallpox epidemic, much to the dismay of the local apothecaries. In 1677 he resigned from his Yorkshire Fellowship because of the obligation to take Holy Orders. Having already set up in medical practice, he did not want to be ordained. He was awarded a Doctor of Medicine in 1682 and moved to London in 1684 at the age of thirty-two.

With his usual eye for business, Radcliffe set up in Bow Street, Covent Garden which was midway between the wealthy and fashionable areas of Westminster and the City. He spent many hours in his local coffee house where he transacted much of his business and in his local tavern where he entertained his guests.

His reputation grew rapidly and there began a long and often stormy relationship with the Royal Family. Radcliffe came to the notice of the future King James II on the King's visit to Oxford in 1683. Three years later James asked him to become physician to his daughter, the Princess Anne (later Queen Anne). Radcliffe resisted the King's pleas to convert him to Catholicism but remained a supporter of James throughout the Glorious Revolution of 1688 when the Protestant William and Mary came to the throne. He was however, physician-in-ordinary to the new King, even though he frequently upset him by his plain speaking.

The Protestant Princess Anne (James II's daughter), who came to the throne on William's death in 1702, suffered poor health. She had married Prince George of Denmark in 1683 and over the next seventeen years was pregnant at least seventeen times, with eleven miscarriages, three stillbirths, and only three live births. In 1691 Radcliffe saved the life of Princess Anne's two-year-old son, the Duke of Gloucester. He was the only one to survive infancy and the hopes for the continuation of the Stuart line rested upon him. The child's aunt, Queen Mary, rewarded Radcliffe with the sum of 1,000 guineas.

In 1694 Radcliffe upset Princess Anne by refusing to attend her when summoned: he was comfortably settled in a drinking establishment, and pronounced her affliction 'the vapours'. She did, however, call on him again in 1700 to attend the young Duke of Gloucester once more. He was always a sickly child, reported to have hydrocephalus. He was taken ill at Windsor during his eleventh birthday party. In the Radcliffe Science Library there is a full report of the case in Radcliffe's own hand. The child complained of pain in his head and was feverish, restless, and light-headed with a rash and difficulty breathing. The attending doctors had applied blisters and, to Radcliffe's annoyance, bled the child before he arrived. Radcliffe suspected smallpox. In consultation with the other doctors, powders were given to make the child sweat and further blisters applied. However, all this was to no avail and the child died. One wonders whether the whole course of history would have changed had Radcliffe been called in earlier and the child survived this illness. However, his health was such that it is unlikely he would have reached adulthood.

Radcliffe had become a Tory Member of Parliament in 1690. He refused a knighthood. Although he never married, he had several love affairs. He became infatuated with one young lady and his friends noticed how he bought a new carriage and a new suit of the latest fashion. But it came to nothing.

In March 1703 he became seriously ill, possibly with pleurisy. He went to Bath to recuperate, and went again the following year. He was, however, so enraged by the prices charged by the lodging house keepers that, in future, he sent his patients to Tunbridge Wells instead, much to the annoyance of the people of Bath.

John Radcliffe was a distant relation of the Earl of Derwentwater, and he sought to cultivate this link, becoming friendly with the Earl's younger son. He even had the family's coat of arms painted on his carriage and engraved on his gold-headed cane (which can be seen at the Royal College of Physicians).

Radcliffe was a shrewd man and not averse to taking risks with his now substantial fortune. He speculated on a number of ventures overseas. His practice was lucrative: by now he was charging as much as £20 a visit. He moved from Bow Street to Bloomsbury Square in 1704 and also bought properties in Hammersmith and Carshalton. In 1711 he purchased the Wolverton Estate in Buckinghamshire for the price of £40,000. He became Tory MP for a Buckingham seat in 1713. In addition he purchased land in Yorkshire and Northamptonshire.

By 1714, Radcliffe's health was declining and he spent more and more time in his house in Carshalton. When Queen Anne was on her deathbed in July 1714 Radcliffe declined, for a number of reasons, to attend when summoned. It was probably mainly his fear of interfering with the official attendants, but also his own ill health, that made him decline. This caused great antipathy, so much so that Radcliffe received death threats. He never really recovered from this and he became depressed and more unwell.

In September 1714 he suffered a mild stroke, and this made him think about writing a will. He had to write it out in his own hand, as he tore the original written by his scrivener Keck. A major stroke followed and he died on All Saints' Day, Monday, 1 November 1714. He was sixty-two years old.

His body was embalmed, awaiting the executors' deliberations over the place of his burial in Oxford and the plans for a ceremonious funeral. The body was brought to Oxford and lay in the Divinity School until 3 December when the funeral took place at the University Church. It was a grand affair, in anticipation of the doctor's benefactions to the university: he had indicated before his death that he would leave money for the building of a new library in Oxford. However, there was some fear of disturbance, possibly because of mixed views of the doctor in the university. So Convocation ordered that members of the university must 'behave themselves in a Manner suitable to so solemn Occasion'. The coffin was buried in front of the organ loft in the University Church, but the planned monument did not materialize and the grave was forgotten. Over a century later it was rediscovered, and an inscription was then engraved in the paving-stone over the grave. Finally, a tablet was erected on the wall near the grave in 1953.

Radcliffe's estate amounted to £140,000. The most touching of his bequests was a sum of £600 per annum to St Bartholomew's Hospital (of which he was a governor) for improving the patients' diet and for buying linen. Nowadays the money is paid into the General Fund which is used mainly for special food and presents for patients at Christmas time. Medical historian, the late Doctor Alastair Robb-Smith, has compared the diet for the poor patients at Bart's before and after Radcliffe's bequest. The amount of wheaten bread was increased by two ounces as was the amount of beef, and a pint of milk potage was added.

There were two main benefactions in Oxford. The first was to University College. He left money for new buildings including a new Master's lodgings at the college and a new quadrangle which was named after its benefactor. He also left money to the college for the establishment of two Radcliffe Travelling Fellowships for recently qualified doctors, a Radcliffe Prize, and a Radcliffe Scholarship in Pharmacology, all of which are still awarded, though the last now as a prize.

Secondly, he left £40,000 for the building of a new library, now called the Radcliffe Camera, which opened in 1749. In the early days it held a rather haphazard collection of books. In the mid-nineteenth century the scientific and medical books were moved to the University Museum and thence in 1902 to the Radcliffe Science Library. The Camera is now a reading room for the Bodleian.

After these benefactions, and legacies and annuities to his family and servants, he left the residue of his estate in trust. It was to be put by the trustees 'to such charitable (purposes) as they in their discretion shall think best'. The first such purpose was the Radcliffe Infirmary. In the 1740s, ideas were circulating about the need for an infirmary in Oxford. The 3rd Earl of Lichfield (see later) was a Radcliffe Trustee and he persuaded his friend Thomas Rowney, MP for the City of Oxford (see later), to donate a piece of land on the Woodstock Road for the building of a voluntary county hospital. The cost of building the hospital was £12,791 15s. 6d., which was financed from the trust. It opened on St Luke's Day, 18 October 1770, and continued to be a world famous hospital until its closure in January 2007. The first phase of the John Radcliffe Hospital, which perpetuates his name, opened in 1972 (the JR1), and the main hospital (JR2) in 1979.

The other important project financed by Doctor Radcliffe's bequest was the building of the Radcliffe Observatory on land adjacent to the Radcliffe Infirmary. It cost over £31,000 and was completed in 1799. In the 1930s the Observatory moved to Pretoria in South Africa where the climate was more suitable for astronomical observations. The Observatory site and buildings were purchased by Sir William Morris, later Lord Nuffield (see section on Nuffield Orthopaedic Centre) in 1930 for a sum of £100,000 and made available for expansion of the Radcliffe Infirmary, and for developing both the Nuffield Institute for Medical Research and the medical school.

The cost of running the Radcliffe Infirmary was passed to the president and governors of the Radcliffe Infirmary in 1884. The majority of the money required for the running of the Radcliffe Camera and the Observatory came from rents from Radcliffe's Wolverton Estate. The trustees were consistently good and generous landlords to the tenants there. The estate survived the vicissitudes of the harvests, and the benefits of the coming of the canal and the railway, but was compulsorily purchased by the Milton Keynes Development Corporation in 1970 for the building of the new town.

Once the Observatory and the Wolverton estate were sold, the trust's income increased greatly. The trustees were in the position of looking for new beneficiaries of Doctor Radcliffe's will, in keeping with his wishes. The trustees have invested in land and in the stock exchange and now make grants to a wide variety of cultural and educational projects. These include, for example, funding apprentices in crafts such as stained glass and sponsoring musicians. All in all, we have a great deal to thank the good doctor for, and I think he would be pleased with the use to which his legacy has been put.

There is a portrait by Sir Godfrey Kneller of John Radcliffe in the Radcliffe Camera above the door into the upper reading room. Inside this reading room above the door is a marble statue by Michael Rysbrack, finished in 1747. There is a copy of the Kneller painting by Michael Dahl in the Level 8 reading room at the Radcliffe Science Library.

We are fortunate to have John Radcliffe's prescription book in the Radcliffe Science Library, written in his own hand. It throws light on his methods of treatment. It is interesting that this was written some eighty years after Harvey's paper on the circulation of the blood (see earlier) which heralded a new scientific approach to medicine. But this was slow to bring about any advances in treatment that would benefit the patient. It is important to note how Radcliffe was beginning to think in systems, like Willis before him, each with their own symptoms and signs. Indeed Radcliffe classifies patients this way in the book. Disorder of a system leads to a specific disease and may be corrected by specific remedies. The same disorder may therefore be recognisable in different patients, and is not merely an imbalance of an individual patient's humours.

But he still depended on treatments such as purging and blisters and to a lesser extent bleeding. There is a detailed discussion in the book of different types of purge and how they affect the different systems of the body. Translation from the Latin by pharmacologists experienced in the history of pharmacology reveals some interesting ingredients. Prescriptions would be made up by an apothecary, and there might be instructions for him to bleed the patient as well. The ingredients do seem on the whole to be quite mild and harmless, which was perhaps why Doctor Radcliffe was a popular doctor.

One of Radcliffe's patients detailed in the prescription book was Sir Isaac Newton, who consulted him for a bronchial complaint. Radcliffe's prescription included 'milk water', which was made by bruising herbs and pouring three gallons of new milk over them, then distilling over a water bath. Pearls and crabs' eyes (part of the head of a crawfish) were ground to a fine powder. Other ingredients were pears and treacle. The exact way in which all these were taken is not clear.

Among other substances Radcliffe prescribed for Newton was ass's milk. It seems that it was used for a variety of ailments from ancient times to the late eighteenth century. This is possibly because it was believed to be the animal milk that most closely resembled human milk. Alternatively it might be because it could be supplied fresh. Cow's milk was often spoiled by the time it reached the patient's home. But Radcliffe kept asses at a farm in Hyde Park Gate and probably had them driven round the streets of London and milked on his patients' doorsteps to ensure a fresh supply of milk!

Thomas Rowney (1693–1759)

Ward 7D at the John Radcliffe Hospital is a medical ward named after Thomas Rowney, who donated a piece of land in St Giles for the building of the Radcliffe Infirmary. The outpatient department at the Radcliffe Infirmary was also named after him.

Thomas Rowney was born in 1693. His father, also called Thomas, was one of the Members of Parliament in Oxford until his death in 1722 when his son took over. Father and son held the seat between them without interruption for sixty-four years.

It seems Thomas (junior) spent some time at Eton College before going on to St John's College, Oxford at the age of sixteen. He became a member of the Inner Temple in 1709.

Thomas Rowney (junior) made two major benefactions to the city of Oxford during his life. The first was for the building of a new town hall in Oxford, opened in 1753, largely at his own expense 'out of great goodwill and affections he has towards the city'. There is a statue of him, erected in the central niche in 1841. Some say the gift was influenced by his wish to endear himself to his constituency in the important general election of 1754.

The second important benefaction was his donation of a piece of land for the building of the Radcliffe Infirmary. In the 1750s, plans were afoot for building a hospital in Oxford. Thomas Rowney owned a five and a quarter acre piece of land called 'Coggin's Piece'. It was an area of open fields (known as the 'Three Farms') in the parish of St Giles. There were gravel pits all round, which were used by the parish for repairing roads. It was a favourite hiding place for highwaymen. In 1758 Rowney donated this land to the trustees of John Radcliffe's will. This gift was very much influenced by his great friendship with the 3rd Earl of Lichfield (see later), who was influential in the building of the Infirmary.

The politics of the time was complicated, the country being divided into two main groups. One faction, known as the 'Old Interest', were Jacobites. They were supporters of James, the Catholic 'Old Pretender', the son of Stuart King James II. The 'New Interest' were supporters of the Hanoverian family, the first of whom, King George I, came to the throne in 1714. Rowney was something of a turncoat. He was described as a 'rough clownish gentleman', a 'rank Jacobite' who had 'drunk the Pretender's health five hundred times'. But when the 'Young Pretender', James's son Bonnie Prince Charlie, came to England, Rowney was terrified and asked his chaplain to pray for King George. But during the 1745 Jacobite rebellion Rowney, with other Tory gentlemen, refused to support the Hanoverians.

Until 1881 Oxford elected two Members of Parliament. At the important general election of 1754, despite support from the local gentry and aristocracy for the New Interest and the Whig party, the Tory party, among whom Rowney was numbered, were victorious. This illustrated the loyalty of the people of Oxford to the Tories and the Old Interest.

Rowney married a Miss Mary Trollope, relatively late in life, on 10 March 1756. There were no children.

1759 was a momentous year. The foundation stone of the Radcliffe Infirmary was laid on 27 August. But it was a sad year in another respect, as on 29 October, Thomas Rowney died in rather unusual circumstances. He was a great friend, neighbour, and political ally of the Earl of Lichfield. Whilst they were out hunting, Thomas Rowney was seized by a violent fit of coughing. He fell from his horse and died instantly. His Lordship and other men were close at hand and a surgeon opened the veins of both arms. It was, however, to no avail. Rowney was about sixty-six years old.

The Rowney family had a country house at Dean, a hamlet in the parish of Spelsbury near Charlbury in Oxfordshire. They also owned land in Oxford. In 1702 his father had built a house, 16 St Giles in Oxford, and Thomas lived there until his death. It was supposed to be the finest of its date in Oxford and would have been something of a rural dwelling when it was built. The dome of the summerhouse in the garden is based on the model for the dome of the Radcliffe Camera. Later the house became known as the 'Judge's Lodgings', as the judge would stay there during the Assizes. In November 1875, Oxford High School for Girls was founded there. In 1965 the house became the property of St John's College. We know from his will that Thomas Rowney also owned land in Warwickshire, Worcestershire, Gloucestershire, and Northumberland.

Thomas Rowney was described as 'a little round and laughing figure'. He was a popular Member of Parliament and much loved by the people of Oxford. He is buried in a vault in St Giles Church with his wife Mary.

Third Earl of Lichfield (1718–1772)

George Henry Lee, 3rd Earl of Lichfield, has played an important part in the history of medicine in Oxford. Most well known is his great influence in the building of the Radcliffe Infirmary, but he also instituted the teaching of medicine on the wards by setting up the Lichfield Clinical Professorship. The Lichfield Day Surgery Unit, in the West Wing of the John Radcliffe Hospital, is named after him as well as medical ward 7F in the main hospital.

He was born on 21 May 1718 in an age when noble status brought power. He had royal blood: his grandmother was a daughter of Charles II by his mistress Barbara Villiers. The family seat was Ditchley Park near Enstone in Oxfordshire. He was educated at Westminster School, then went up to St John's College, Oxford in 1736, receiving his MA in 1737. He married Diana, daughter of Sir Thomas Frankland, but sadly they had no children. His wife was descended from Oliver Cromwell.

In 1740 he was elected MP for the County of Oxfordshire, sitting until 1743 when his father died and he succeeded to the Earldom. As a young man he promoted the Jacobean cause and showed great promise in the Tory party. He was described as 'handsome, lively and agreeable'. He was interested in the arts and was a fellow of the Society of Antiquaries and vice-president of the Society of Arts. On the death of George II in 1760, there were great political manoeuvrings and the old Whig supremacy was at an end. Lord Lichfield became a favourite of the new King George III. Among other posts he was made a Lord of the Bedchamber and a Privy Councillor. In 1762 he became Chancellor of Oxford University.

In 1755 at the age of only thirty-seven he was appointed a Radcliffe Trustee (see earlier) and soon became chairman. There are records of a mention of the desirability of an infirmary in Oxford as far back as 1743. However, it was at a meeting of the trustees in Lichfield's house on 26 April 1758 that an order was signed for £4,000 to build a hospital in Oxford. From the first, Lord Lichfield and fellow trustee William Cartwright were entrusted with the local supervision of the building.

It was through Lord Lichfield that the land for the Infirmary was made available. Thomas Rowney, MP for the City of Oxford (see earlier), was a neighbour of Lichfield, and a close friend and fellow Tory. They hunted together and were drinking companions. Lichfield persuaded his friend Rowney to donate Coggin's Piece, a five-acre plot of land in St Giles, for the building of the hospital. Lichfield continued to be involved as the Infirmary progressed.

There was a meeting of well-wishers in the 'Star and Garter' tavern in Pall Mall on 3 April 1770, six months before the hospital opened. Following this a list of subscribers was published which showed that the Earl and the Countess of Lichfield each gave an annual subscription of £10 10s. 0d. Lord Lichfield was elected President of the Governors in July and the women's ward was named Lichfield Ward.

In July 1771, there was a service at the University Church to celebrate the opening of the Infirmary, and Lord Lichfield provided a 'brace of bucks' for the feast for the governors that followed.

Lord Lichfield died aged fifty-three on 9 September 1772, two years after the Infirmary opened. He suffered a lengthy illness and died at the Hot Springs of Clifton.

From the earliest days of the Radcliffe Infirmary, it had been intended that it should provide opportunities for the teaching of undergraduates. Lord Lichfield had this very much in mind and left a sum of £7,000 in his will for the establishment of the Lichfield Clinical Professorship (although it was not established until after the death of the Countess in 1779). The monies from the sale of his London house were put in trust, to be used to fund a professorship for the reading of clinical lectures in physic. The holder of the post was to be a university professor on the staff of the Infirmary. The holder must have had a degree in physic for at least five years and was chosen by the members of Convocation.

On the days when patients were admitted to the Infirmary, the Lichfield Professor could take interesting cases under his care and use them for the instruction of the students. He was required to attend these patients daily on the ward with his students. Finally, he must read a lecture twice weekly on these patients during winter months.

The Lichfield Clinical Professorship was a significant step forward in the training of medical students. In fact, it was the first academic post in this country that was specifically for clinical instruction of students on the wards and at the bedside. (In America it was not until the late nineteenth century that Osler brought teaching to the bedside.)

There was a Lichfield Professor continuously for a hundred years. Then in 1883 it was divided into two Lichfield Lectureships held in turn by members of the honorary medical and surgical staff. Then in 1948 the statute was changed again and one or two Lichfield Lectures are now delivered each year by distinguished visiting teachers, potential applicants being nominated by heads of department.

Lord Lichfield was an innovator, and a man of great foresight. He was the driving force behind the Radcliffe Infirmary and turned the dream into reality. He was a diligent Radcliffe Trustee and never missed a meeting. He was a man of great influence in the country, though some felt he did not fulfil his early promise in the Tory party.

There is a splendid neo-Classical monument to him in the parish church of All Saints, Spelsbury, near Ditchley Park in Oxfordshire. His lengthy epitaph, carried on a long scroll by a cherub, was possibly written by the poet Thomas Warton, sometime Poet Laureate, who was rector of a nearby parish. It describes Lichfield as combining 'dignity with ease', 'affability with propriety', and 'good senses with graces of wit'. James Boswell described him as 'a most humane, agreeable man'. Horace Walpole noted his 'sagacity, good taste' and promotion of the Jacobean cause, while another described him as 'a red faced old gentleman shaking all over with the palsy'.

There is no doubt that he was a public-spirited man and able to pull all sides together in support of the hospital. In addition to his position at the Radcliffe Infirmary, he was president of the Bethlem Hospital and vice-president of the Smallpox Hospital. He seems to have been a kindly man, leaving money in his will for the care of his horses after his death, 'so long as life can be made agreeable to them'. There is a portrait of Lord Lichfield by an unknown artist at the John Radcliffe Hospital in the corridor between the West Wing and the main hospital.

The Earldom became extinct in 1776 and Ditchley Park became the seat of the Viscounts Dillon. It is worth noting that George Henry Lee is not related to the present Earls of Lichfield who are of a different family.

There seems to be considerable confusion over the spelling of the name 'Lichfield'. At the Radcliffe Infirmary there was great indecision. Thus some signs to the Lichfield Unit used a 't' and some did not! In the West Wing at the John Radcliffe Hospital it is spelt without the 't', so this spelling has been used here.

Fourth Duke of Marlborough (1739–1817)

Marlborough Ward, Ward 6F at the John Radcliffe Hospital, is a surgical ward named after George Spencer, 4th Duke of Marlborough. A keen astronomer, he provided land for the building of the Radcliffe Observatory (which later became part of the Radcliffe Infirmary and then Green Templeton College).

The 4th Duke was born on 26 January 1739. He was educated at Eton, then entered the Coldstream Guards in 1755, becoming a Captain the following year. He inherited the Dukedom in 1758. He took his seat in the House of Lords and became Lord Lieutenant of Oxfordshire. He became a noted courtier and politician. Indeed, he was chosen to bear the sceptre at the coronation of King George III in 1761. He was made Lord Chamberlain and Lord Privy Seal and then in 1768, Knight of the Garter.

The 4th Duke was involved in the building of the Radcliffe Infirmary right from the beginning. Thus he was one of the original twenty-four subscribers who met at a rather grand tavern called the 'Star and Garter' in Pall Mall on 3 April 1770. The Duke himself was the most generous subscriber, pledging the sum of £76 per year. Following this meeting, an advertisement was issued seeking subscriptions to the charity. The Duke became President of the Radcliffe Infirmary in 1772 following the death of the Earl of Lichfield (see earlier). In 1786 he was elected to the Royal Society.

He was a learned and scholarly man. A keen amateur astronomer, he built a private observatory at his home in Blenheim Palace. When there was talk of building an observatory with part of John Radcliffe's bequest, he stepped in. In November 1770 he took a twenty-year lease from St John's College of some forty acres of farmland to the north of the Radcliffe Infirmary. His plan was to make part of it, a little over nine acres adjacent to the hospital, known as the 'Garden Piece', available for the trustees of John Radcliffe's estate. They could then build the Observatory there when they were ready. In July 1771 the Court of Chancery gave sanction for expenditure and work began. The trustees were concerned, as early as 1777, that it was only the leasehold that the Duke had purchased, but it took until 1821 for the freehold of the land to be acquired.

There is a sad story about the Duke's telescope. He owned a rather superior twelve-foot Gregorian reflecting telescope which he donated to the Radcliffe Observatory. A visiting astronomer noticed in 1777 that it was still in its packing case. Nearly a century later, it was discovered again by a later observer, lying forgotten in a corner of the photographic room. It was decided, however, that the expense involved in hiring additional staff to operate it was too great, so it was never used.

In 1762 the Duke had married Lady Caroline Russell and they had eight children. He died on 29 January 1817 at Blenheim Palace at the age of seventy-eight. He is buried there. On his death he was followed by his son as President of the Radcliffe Infirmary.

Seventh Duke of Marlborough (1822–1883)

Mention must also be made of the 7th Duke, John Winston Spencer-Churchill, who became a Radcliffe Trustee in 1863. He was educated at Eton and Oriel College, Oxford. He was a member of parliament until he became Duke when he entered the House of Lords. He was a committed conservative. He attended the meetings of the trustees regularly till he became Lord Lieutenant of Ireland in 1876. In his later years he was not such an assiduous attender. He died on 4 July 1883 at the age of sixty-one.

Marquis of Blandford (1686–1703)

Finally, mention must be made of a connection between the Marlborough family and John Radcliffe. The 1st Duke of Marlborough was one of Europe's greatest generals. He is best known for his victory over the French at the Battle of Blenheim in 1704. Although he was already an Earl, Queen Anne created the Dukedom. In recognition of his achievements, she built and furnished Blenheim Palace for him in Woodstock near Oxford at her own expense.

The Duchess, Sarah Jennings, was initially a great friend and favourite of Queen Anne, and indeed this helped the rise of the Duke. But Sarah was a hot-headed woman, and her friendship with the Queen was a stormy one. At one stage she was dismissed from court.

The only surviving son and heir apparent of the 1st Duke was John Churchill, Marquis of Blandford. He was keen to enter the army and pursue a military career like his father. However, his mother was anxious about the risk. So he went up to King's College, Cambridge in 1700. Early in 1703 he contracted smallpox. The Duchess went straight to his bedside, and Queen Anne dispatched her personal doctors. The story goes that among the doctors she summoned was John Radcliffe. The Duchess pleaded with him to come. However, Radcliffe said he had some seriously ill patients in London whom he could not leave so he would not go to Cambridge. He did send directions for the boy's treatment, but it is said that these were ignored. The Marquis died on 20 February 1703 at the age of only seventeen. His parents were distraught. It seems he was a promising young man, described by one acquaintance as 'the most agreeable but the most free thinking and reasonable creature that one can imagine for his age'.

The Reverend Doctor Frederick Barnes (1771–1859)

The Barnes Unit, the Oxford Hospitals Liaison Psychiatry Service at the John Radcliffe Hospital, is named after Doctor Barnes who was a canon and subdean of Christ Church.

Frederick Barnes was born in St Merrin in Cornwall in 1771. He attended Westminster School before coming up to Christ Church in 1790. He received his BA in 1797 and his BD in 1805. He was appointed a canon of Christ Church in 1810, becoming Doctor of Divinity the following year. He became one of the longest serving canons of Christ Church. He was also at some stage Chaplain to the House of Commons and was Rector of Bishop's Cheriton and Colyton in Devon.

He had connections with the Warneford Asylum (then called the Oxford Lunatic Asylum) in its early days, probably because he was a man of prominence in Oxford. He was chairman of the Building Committee and served on the Committee of Management. It is likely that he was a benefactor. When the unit at the John Radcliffe was planned, the name was suggested by Doctor William Parry-Jones, former consultant psychiatrist at the Warneford Hospital, because of Doctor Barnes's connection with psychiatry in Oxford.

It is interesting that from 1796 to 1802, before he was ordained, Doctor Barnes was a Major in the University Volunteers (the forerunner of the Oxford University Officer Training Corps). This was a time when Britain was in the midst of the Napoleonic Wars.

There is a memorial to Doctor Barnes in the Latin Chapel in Christ Church Cathedral. There is also a drawing of him in the college archive.

Lord Joseph Lister (1827–1912)

Ward 6A at the John Radcliffe Hospital is a surgical ward named after Joseph Lister, surgeon and pioneer of antisepsis. His work in promoting the antiseptic method went a long way towards making surgery a safe treatment.

Lister was born on 5 April 1827 at Upton in Essex to a family of successful businessmen. His father was a self-educated amateur natural historian who made improvements to the microscope and was a Fellow of the Royal Society, and his mother was a teacher.

The family were Quakers. This gave Joseph a very devout and simple but happy and stable life. However it did limit the occupations open to him when he left school. Quakers could not be lawyers, judges, or civil servants because they would not take a civil oath. The armed services were ruled out because the Quakers could not bear arms. There were no ordained clergy in the Quakers. Furthermore, the universities only admitted Anglicans. Thus business and trade were the fields most of them chose. However, Joseph wanted to be a surgeon from an early age. Whilst many doctors and surgeons of the time did not have a formal medical education, this was the route he wanted to take. He was fortunate that in 1826, University College, London had been founded, to provide an education for people of non-Anglican denominations and of other faiths.

Joseph entered the university in March 1844 at the age of sixteen.

He was a serious, hard-working student and took his BA in 1847. However, just as he started his clinical medical studies, he caught smallpox, and it seems that this, together with the effect of three years of hard study, led to a nervous breakdown. He spent time resting and travelled to Ireland, and by the end of 1848 he was back at university. He passed his BM in 1852 and also passed his exams for membership of the Royal College of Surgeons. He found time for research and published his first paper, on the microscopic examination of the muscles of the iris.

His professor in London advised him to gain experience in Edinburgh, and James Syme, Professor of Clinical Surgery there, took him under his wing. In 1855 Syme made him his 'extramural lecturer'. Lister took this very seriously, choosing the topical subject of inflammation for his lectures. In 1856 he married Professor Syme's daughter Agnes. As she was not a Quaker, he had to resign from the Society of Friends. The same year he was elected assistant surgeon to the Edinburgh Royal Infirmary where he continued to be busy with his hospital work, his lectures, and his research on coagulation.

In 1860 he was appointed Regius Professor of Surgery at the University of Glasgow, where his lectures were well received. He was a successful teacher and surgeon, but in his heart he felt he was really a researcher.

The subject in which he was to make his name was antisepsis. Surgery had made great strides with the introduction of anaesthesia. Operations could take longer, and there was time for more care such as tying up blood vessels. But its scope was limited by the huge problem of wound infection. One surgeon wrote that those entering hospital for surgery were more at risk of death than the soldier on the field of Waterloo.

In the 1840s, Semmelweis in Vienna had observed that puerperal fever was commoner in the women attended by the medical students, many of whom had come straight from doing autopsies. He had introduced disinfection with chlorine, with great success. Others had used antiseptics through the years, even the Greeks applying wine and vinegar to wounds. Lister observed infection on his wards and noted that it was worse if beds were close together or if the patient was in a bed next to a patient with infection. In general, doctors and nurses did not wash their hands between patients. Lister introduced some cleanliness measures such as hand-washing, rather to the amusement and derision of his fellow surgeons, but the results were not good.

People dreaded coming into hospital for surgery and many chose to have their operation at home or in the surgeon's private rooms.

Lister noticed that it was compound rather than simple fractures that became infected and he wondered if it was something in the hospital air (termed 'miasma') that was responsible. Then Lister became aware of the work of the French chemist and biologist Louis Pasteur. Pasteur had become interested in the subject of fermentation, including alcoholic fermentation and milk fermentation. In his studies he showed that it was not the air itself, but living micro-organisms within the air that caused fermentation and also putrefaction of food. He showed that heating liquid to 60 degrees centigrade ('pasteurisation') checked their growth. He was later to publish his germ theory of disease.

Lister saw the importance of this work, and believed that if these germs could be prevented from getting into an open wound or could be destroyed after, then the problem of wound infection could be solved. He dedicated the rest of his life to this. He realised he couldn't use heat on wounds, but he had heard of the chemical carbolic acid which had been successfully used in the 1830s to kill entozoa that had been causing disease in cattle. In 1865 Lister began to use it on compound fractures. His first case was a failure. But then he tried it on a boy who had a compound fracture of the tibia, following being run over by a cart. His wound healed without infection. Results were mixed, but there were cases where patients were saved from amputation.

Despite these successes, Lister's work was not taken seriously by many. He published a series of papers in the *Lancet* on the subject in 1867 in which he described his method in detail. On compound fractures he would dip a rag in full strength carbolic acid and apply it to all accessible parts of the wound. For medium-sized wounds he would apply a lint dressing soaked in carbolic acid to the wound and place a tin cap over the top, so protecting it from the air and from evaporation. For larger wounds, he made a paste of a mixture of carbolic acid, carbonate of lime, and linseed oil, which was placed between two layers of thin calico and placed over the wound. It acted as a reservoir of the carbolic acid. The technique involved both antisepsis (killing bacteria within the wound) and asepsis (preventing bacteria getting in to the wound).

In an address in 1867 he reported that over the last nine months during which he had used the antiseptic treatment, he had had no cases of pyaemia, gangrene, or erysipelas among his patients. Of eleven cases of compound fracture, none had died. However, there was still little interest at home and he was ridiculed by many. Indeed the hospital management were angry because they thought it was a slur on their reputation. More interest was shown on the continent.

Lister returned to Edinburgh as Professor of Surgery in 1869. It had been the leading medical school in Britain for a hundred years. He was respected and admired by the students and indeed, most of them accepted the germ theory and the antiseptic method. He tried using carbolic acid in the operating theatre, spraying it from a pump. He would dress the wound himself and check it post-operatively on the ward round.

It is interesting, however, that other measures that seem elementary to us were not in use. Thus Lister would operate in his street clothes and while he washed his hands, he did not scrub them. Some surgeons used masks and gowns and rubber gloves, though this was by no means universal. It was very much a time of transition in the field of antisepsis and surgery.

Lister's patients loved him. Despite an aloofness, he had a gentle manner and cared about his patients' comfort. He even sewed on the leg of a distraught little girl's doll. Sadly he and Agnes did not have any children themselves. He was much affected when a patient died, reviewing the notes to see if anything could have been done better. He was surgeon to Queen Victoria and operated on her at Balmoral. He did, however refuse to agree to her request to publically oppose vivisection.

Visitors came from all over the world to see Lister's work but surgeons at home were still sceptical. At British Medical Association annual meetings in 1871 and 1873, he made little impression, but by the 1875 meeting in Edinburgh, he gave a practical demonstration which was well received. When he travelled to meetings abroad, it was something of a triumphal march.

To the surprise of many, he accepted the Chair of Surgery at King's College Hospital in London and moved there in 1877, maybe because he was anxious to win over the medical profession in London. He had some success and the famous surgeon Sir James Paget said in 1879 that he had made the most important achievement in surgery. Even his old adversary the *Lancet* said that the antiseptic method had 'revolutionised modern surgery'. He had made possible operations on the chest, abdomen, and brain, areas previously closed to surgery because of the risk of infection. It was only surgery on the extremities that had been possible before. Now, instead of being a last resort, surgery could be an acceptable treatment of choice.

The tide had turned. Many honours were bestowed upon him, including honorary degrees from Oxford and Cambridge. He was made a baronet. Despite all this, he remained modest and diffident, his whole purpose being to prevent the suffering of his fellow men. He retired in 1892. Later that year, he went to Paris for the official celebrations for Pasteur's seventieth birthday. It was a splendid affair and Lister had been asked to make an address. Afterwards, Pasteur embraced him warmly. After retirement, he helped set up the British Institute of Preventive Medicine which was later named the Lister Institute.

Joseph and Agnes loved walking and bird-watching, and enjoyed travelling abroad. In 1893, Agnes died of pneumonia in Italy. Joseph was devastated. Not only was she a dearly beloved wife, but she had also been a constant help to him in his work. She would make notes for him, sitting up till the early hours of the morning as he worked through the night. She encouraged him when for so long his work was not recognised.

Joseph never recovered from his loss. Despite becoming President of the Royal Society and of the British Association for the Advancement of Science, his heart had gone out of it. He was the first surgeon to be made a peer of the realm. He became increasingly lonely and reclusive, and spent a lot of time in the spa town of Buxton. In 1903 he became ill with what he thought was a stroke, and was never the same again. His hearing and eyesight were gone and he could no longer read or write. He stayed at Walmer in Kent, spending time sitting on the beach. He finally died in his sleep there on 10 February 1912 at the age of eighty-four.

His obituary in the *Lancet* described him as 'the greatest modern Englishman' and 'the world's greatest surgeon'. On 16 February there was a public funeral at Westminster Abbey, attended by representatives of the King and Queen and by the Prime Minister. He declined burial there, instead being laid to rest in West Hampstead Cemetery.

Sir William Osler (1849–1919)

Sir William Osler was Regius Professor of Medicine in Oxford from 1905 to 1919.

The medical students' club at the John Radcliffe Hospital is named after him and there is an Osler Road nearby.

William Osler was born on 12 July 1849 in Bond Head, a hamlet north of Toronto in the wilds of Canada. His father was a clergyman, originally from Cornwall, who moved to Canada as a missionary. Osler went to several schools where he was always up to pranks. At his last school he was greatly influenced by the founder, a clergyman, and by the school physician, both of whom nurtured his interest in natural history and introduced him to the microscope. In 1867 he went up to the University of Trinity College in Toronto, initially to prepare for the ministry. However, he became interested in science and in the burning issues of the day, including Darwin's theories. He decided he wanted to be a doctor and commenced medical training first in Toronto then at McGill University in Montreal.

During his time at McGill he developed his interest in pathology and the importance of correlating the clinical picture with post-mortem findings. He excelled in his final year thesis on this subject. He qualified in 1872 and the next year, like many American and Canadian students, travelled to Europe to gain postgraduate training.

He did research, attended courses, and worked on the wards. In

London, Osler was the first to show what were later called 'platelets' as discrete bodies in circulating blood. In Berlin he was greatly impressed by the great scientist and pathologist Virchow who developed his 'cell theory'.

Osler returned to McGill in the spring of 1874 and soon became Professor in the Institutes of Medicine (physiology and histology). He was an inspiring teacher and even purchased microscopes for the use of the medical students at his own expense. He maintained his interest in clinicopathology, doing over a hundred post-mortems a year. He was also physician to the smallpox ward and chief physician at the Montreal General Hospital. Here he began his teaching at the bedside.

During his years at McGill he established himself as an able clinician and scientist who published widely and was recognised in Europe as well as North America. In 1884 he revisited Europe at an exciting time following Koch's discovery of the tubercle bacillus and when scientists were demonstrating the role of bacteria in infectious diseases.

Later that year he was appointed Professor of Clinical Medicine at the University of Pennsylvania. In 1885 he had the honour of delivering the Gulstonian Lectures at the Royal College of Physicians in London. He chose the subject of malignant endocarditis, a somewhat baffling (though not uncommon) condition at the time and fraught with complications of nomenclature and classification. It is a disease where the heart valves (or lining of the heart) become infected so that ulceration and growth of vegetations occurs on the endothelial lining. These may embolise and cause a variety of symptoms ranging from a purpuric rash to hemiplegia.

Osler had begun his studies on endocarditis at McGill, again studying both the clinical features and the pathology. In his lectures, he reported on a series of 209 cases. The greatness of Osler's lectures lay in the clarity with which he described the condition bringing it to the attention of the medical profession and making it understandable. In 1909 Osler reported on ten chronic cases in which, for up to twelve months, a fever was the main symptom. The condition could be confused with other infectious diseases including malaria, typhoid, and even tuberculosis. The late onset of the cardiac signs made it difficult to diagnose except in cases where there was marked embolisation.

However, there is another clue to diagnosis. In 1888 Osler had visited a twenty-eight-year-old patient of a Doctor Mullen in Hamilton, Ontario. Doctor Mullen drew Osler's attention to tender erythematous spots or nodules in the skin of the patient, on the fingers and toes. Doctor Mullen described how he had noted that these could last for anything from a few hours to a week. They can vary in size from a pinhead to a centimetre and a half and are believed to be due to emboli. Over the following years Osler noticed these in other cases, and drew attention to them as a useful sign in the diagnosis of this difficult disease. They became known as 'Osler's Nodes'.

In 1888 he was invited to become physician-in-chief at the newly established flagship Johns Hopkins Hospital in Baltimore, Maryland. He was also to be the first Professor of the Theory and Practice of Medicine at the medical school. Whilst waiting for the medical school to open, Osler wrote his textbook *The Principles and Practice of Medicine*. On completing the textbook in 1892, Osler proposed for the second time to Grace Revere Linzee Gross, widow of Doctor Samuel W. Gross, a member of a renowned Philadelphia medical family. She was the great-granddaughter of Paul Revere, famed for riding to warn the patriots that the British were coming in the American War of Independence. They married a few months later.

At Johns Hopkins the staff, particularly Osler, revolutionised the teaching of medicine in North America. In Europe students were given a good scientific grounding and had contact with patients on the wards. Up until then, medical training in America lagged far behind, some students qualifying simply after attending a course of lectures. Osler said that he would like to be remembered for bringing the teaching of medicine to the bedside. He introduced clinical laboratories and clerkships where students were given responsibility for patient care.

Osler had become a celebrity and one of the best-known and best-loved physicians in North America and Britain. He travelled widely attending meetings, lecturing, and giving consultations. However, he could not carry on at this pace. He was finding life stressful and suffering from angina. He and Grace realised that he needed to slow down. A solution arose: he was being considered for the post of Regius Professor of Medicine at Oxford. During his visit to Oxford in 1904, he received a formal offer from Arthur Balfour, British Prime Minister. Grace was adamant he should accept, for his health's sake. She wired him from home: 'Do not procrastinate. Better go in a steamer than go in a pine-box'. Osler saw the appeal, partly the lighter duties, but also the proximity of the Bodleian Library, and the good secondhand book sellers in Europe (for he was already an avid book-collector).

They were sad to leave Baltimore. However, in May 1905 they arrived in Oxford, together with their nine-year-old son Edward Revere Osler. The next year they bought 13 Norham Gardens in North Oxford. They had extensive alterations made to the house before they moved in, and there is a photograph of the hundred or so workmen taken at a dinner the Oslers gave for them. The building firm is still in operation.

Osler threw himself into the academic and social life of Oxford. His main task as Regius Professor was his course of teaching clinics at the Radcliffe Infirmary, where he was a consultant. The highlight of the week was the clinic on Sunday mornings which was attended by local GPs and by Oxford students doing their clinical training in London.

He was an ex-officio curator of the Bodleian Library, a position he relished. He organised an appeal, giving generously from his own pocket, to purchase a Shakespeare First Folio for the library. It was one that had been discarded after the Restoration and was now offered to the Bodleian for sale. The cost was £3,000. He was a delegate of the Oxford University Press. As Regius Professor he was a student (fellow) of Christ Church. He was a kindly examiner, who felt that exams could stifle the development of the student.

13 Norham Gardens became known as the 'Open Arms' because of the hospitality shown to so many. Grace was always a great support to her husband, entertaining guests while he slipped away to work in his study after dinner. The house bustled with medical students, Rhodes Scholars, colleagues, and family and friends from all over the world. Books from Osler's extensive library would be consulted over dinner and all manner of subjects discussed. Their son, known as Revere, attended Winchester College where, however, he did not shine

academically. He later developed a passion for books, much to his father's delight.

As Regius Professor, Osler was Master of the Almshouses at Ewelme (a village some fourteen miles south of Oxford). He took his duties very seriously, visiting frequently and looking after the old gentlemen. There is a memorial tablet to Sir William, Grace, and Revere inside the church. He cared for many notable patients in Oxford and beyond. William Morris (later Lord Nuffield) and James Murray, Editor of the Oxford English Dictionary, were among them as well as Edward, Prince of Wales (later Edward VIII). Osler was knighted in 1911.

When war broke out in 1914, gloom descended on Sir William and Lady Osler. They felt great sorrow and foreboding at the suffering and loss of life to come. As well as their normal work, they both became busy with war work and with the constant demands of friends, relatives, colleagues, refugees, and acquaintances. The 'Open Arms' was busier than ever and though they put on a brave face, they felt the constant strain.

Osler was Honorary Colonel in the Territorial Army and so was official consultant to the military hospitals in Oxford. The Examination Schools, Town Hall, and various college grounds had been hastily converted to hospitals. In addition he was advisor to a number of Canadian and American military hospitals in Britain. As advisor on public health he campaigned for vaccination against typhoid, traditionally the scourge of armies, and also helped the War Office amass information for a history of the war.

The war brought great personal sadness to the Oslers. Revere interrupted his studies at Christ Church after a term and joined up. In August 1917 he was with his unit near Ypres when he was severely injured. He was operated on but died a few hours later. Harvey Cushing, friend of the family, and later biographer of Osler, was present at his death. Sir William never really recovered from this tragedy. Grace was at his side to support him, but he was a broken man.

After the war, he found solace in organising his library. He had, however, always been prone to bronchitis. Over the summer of 1919 he was unwell and from September he was bedridden. The final illness was possibly initially caused by influenza infection. It developed into empyema and multiple abscess formation in the lungs. Fluid was aspirated from the pleural cavity on several occasions and two operations were performed to open up the pleural cavity, but to no avail. He haemorrhaged from the wound after the second operation and died on 29 December 1919 at his home.

His funeral took place at Christ Church Cathedral and hundreds of people attended. His favourite book, Thomas Browne's *Religio medici*, was placed on his coffin. Grace lived on until 31 August 1928 when she died peacefully at home after a stroke.

As the years went by, Osler had become increasingly interested in the history of medicine. He donated his library of over seven thousand books (some very rare and sought-after) to the University of McGill to form a library of the history of medicine. Dr. William Francis, a relation of Osler, stayed at the 'Open Arms' while compiling the *Bibliotheca Osleriana*, the catalogue of the Osler Library. The books were shipped to Canada and the Osler Library was opened in May 1929. Sir William's ashes were taken there too, where they remain to this day. (His brain was preserved and taken to the Wistar Institute in Philadelphia to be studied.)

Osler was possibly the most well-known and best-loved doctor of his age and still ranks among the greatest. There are Osler Societies in America, London, and Japan to this day. It is interesting to ponder why. Perhaps the answer is that he excelled in so many fields. He was an able scientist. At the same time he was a man of great humanity. On one occasion he was chided for whistling as he left a dying patient's room. He replied that if he did not whistle he would cry. He had application and a capacity for hard work. He was a charismatic teacher, inspiring the young to achieve great things. He had an attractive, sociable personality with always a kind word, both for patients and colleagues.

At his speech at his farewell dinner in New York in 1905, he had enunciated his three personal ideals: firstly, to do the day's work well without worrying about the morrow. Secondly, to act honourably to his colleagues and patients. Thirdly, to cultivate such equanimity as to enable him to bear success with humility and sorrow with courage.

He also lives on in his writings. His textbook, the *Principles and Practice of Medicine*, has had a huge influence on generations of doctors. It was an immediate success and went through many editions, only going out of print in 1947. It has been translated into various languages, including Chinese. It even prompted the founding of the Rockefeller Institute and Foundation: Rockefeller's advisor was transfixed when he happened to read it, and noting the lack of therapy for so many illnesses, saw the need for scientific research.

During his life Osler wrote and delivered a huge number of papers and talks on all manner of subjects, scientific, classical, philosophical, and literary. As we have seen, he was a physician in a changing world, living through an age of great change, social, medical, and technological. In his early years, he was known to bleed patients. Later some termed him a 'therapeutic nihilist', but it is probably rather the case that he shunned many of the useless remedies prevalent at the time. But the world of scientific medicine was unfolding. He saw the development of germ theory of disease, the widespread use of the microscope, and the introduction of X-rays. Training of doctors and nurses improved during his lifetime, both becoming respected professions. He saw the invention of the telephone, the aeroplane, and the motor car and lived through the First World War, after which the world was never the same again. He embraced motoring enthusiastically, travelling in his Renault up to Scotland for holidays, and regularly to the almshouses at Ewelme. He was a member of the Royal Automobile Club. The young William Morris (later to be Lord Nuffield) looked after the car, and this led to a friendship between the two men that later led to Lord Nuffield's great medical benefactions.

There are two diseases named after Osler. The first, 'Osler–Vaquez disease', a form of polycythaemia, is a condition described by Osler in 1903 as 'Chronic Cyanosis, with Polycythaemia and Enlarged Spleen: A New Clinical Entity'. The second, 'Osler–Weber–Rendu disease', is a condition of multiple hereditary haemorrhagic telangiectasia of which Osler made a study.

An area in which Osler took a great interest was the treatment of tuberculosis, the 'white plague'. It is easy for us to forget the fear and suffering attending the disease. Osler was always saddened when a medical student or doctor succumbed. At McGill and Philadelphia he studied the pathology of the disease in the numerous post-mortems he carried out. Koch isolated the bacillus in 1882 and Osler was one of the first in America to demonstrate the bacillus in clinical specimens. When it became clear that the hopes of tuberculin as a miracle cure were unfounded, Osler became convinced of the importance of public health measures. While at the Johns Hopkins, he instigated a public health campaign on a local and national level. It included female medical students visiting patients at home and advising on cleanliness, diet, and fresh air. In 1901 he felt it possible that 'the Captain of the men of death', as John Bunyan had dubbed consumption, might be reduced to 'private' and then 'drummed out of the regiment'.

He carried on this crusade in Oxford, working tirelessly. He stressed the importance of education of doctors and the public. Thus in 1909, he organised a public exhibition on tuberculosis in the Examination Schools and the following year he founded the Oxfordshire County Association for the Prevention of Tuberculosis. It is notable that considerable improvements in outcomes followed, long before the era of antibiotics. He set up a tuberculosis dispensary at the Radcliffe Infirmary and rural ones throughout the county. He frequently visited these and even did home visits. Initially inpatients were treated on verandas at the Radcliffe Infirmary but more space was needed. Osler played an important part in the purchase of the Manor House Estate in Headington (where the John Radcliffe is now) for the building of a TB sanatorium. It was called the Osler Pavilion but was sadly not completed till some eight years after Osler's death. It closed in 1969.

13 Norham Gardens was left by the Oslers for the use of Regius Professors of Medicine. It is now owned by Green Templeton College, and many books, papers, photographs, and other artefacts connected with the Oslers may be seen there. There is a portrait of Sir William by Seymour Thomas in the Level 8 Reading Room at the Radcliffe Science Library.

Doctor William Collier (1856–1935)

Ward 7E, an acute general medical ward at the John Radcliffe Hospital, is named after William Collier, who was a physician at the Radcliffe Infirmary from 1885 to 1921.

William was born in Cambridgeshire in 1856. He was educated at Sherborne School, then Jesus College, Cambridge. He was the first Cambridge graduate to be elected to the Radcliffe Infirmary staff. He had no clear idea of what he wanted to do whilst at Cambridge, but excelled at sport. He was an athletics blue and also represented the university on a fifty-mile penny-farthing cycle race. He interrupted his studies to go on an expedition to the Sahara but didn't get far because he suffered from seasickness.

He finally decided he wanted to do medicine, and did his clinical training at King's College, London, qualifying in 1880. He was a dresser to Joseph Lister whilst there.

In 1881 he became house physician at the Radcliffe Infirmary, and remained there for the rest of his life. He started off in general practice before being appointed to the staff in 1885.

He was an excellent physician and able teacher, and his opinion was often sought. He was widely admired as a man of skill and integrity. He was enthusiastic and idealistic and his strong views and argumentative nature belied a kind and sympathetic character. He could sometimes be gruff in manner which some patients found disconcerting. He had a reputation for absent-mindedness and on one occasion during the First World War appeared at the military hospital in correct military attire but a bowler hat.

He played an important part in the running of the Radcliffe Infirmary and with the treasurer, the Reverend George Cronshaw, introduced the 'Twopenny Contributory Scheme', where people were asked to give 2d. a week towards the running of the hospital. After the war, the finances of the Infirmary were in a sorry state. Many of the older subscribers had died and the increased cost of living meant that few of the middle classes came forward. Furthermore, the cost of treatment per patient had risen.

William Collier announced the new scheme in April 1920. It was modelled on the one recently set up in Leicester, but the Oxford one was the first scheme introduced in a rural area. Collier chaired the special committee, and he and other members of the hospital staff toured the villages, explaining the scheme which was on the whole warmly received. This pioneering scheme saved the Radcliffe Infirmary from financial disaster. By 1923 the contributions were providing 60 per cent of the total hospital income and once again, income was exceeding expenditure. Collier took a great part in the organisation of the hospital and encouraged economy, for example keeping an eye open for unnecessary lights on or dripping taps.

He maintained his interest in sport, including mountaineering and golf. He was a keen motorcyclist and the family had to sell his motorcycle when he reached old age and they felt he was not safe to ride it any more.

Collier was one of the founding members of the 'Medical Club' in Oxford and of the Oxford Medical Society. He held the Lichfield Lectureship for several years. He was a Fellow of the Royal College of Physicians.

He was asked to preside over the British Medical Association's annual meeting in Oxford in 1904. His presidential address was on the subject of the growth and development of the medical school in Oxford. The address and indeed the whole meeting was a great success. It was at this meeting that Sir William Osler made up his mind that he would accept the offer of Regius Professor of Medicine.

During the First World War, Collier was a Lieutenant Colonel in the Royal Army Medical Corps and was in charge of the 3rd Southern General Hospital in Oxford.

After his retirement from the Radcliffe Infirmary in 1921, he continued to be a member of the Committee of Management and was Vice-President of the hospital.

William died on 21 December 1935. His wife Anna was daughter of the Reverend Doctor James Legge who was the Professor of Chinese at Oxford. They had three sons and two daughters. Their son William also became a Fellow of the Royal College of Physicians.

Field Marshal Earl Alexander of Tunis (1891–1969)

This is something of a puzzle. Ward 7C at the John Radcliffe Hospital is a medical ward called Alexander Ward, but it is not clear after whom it is named. One possibility is that it is named after Earl Alexander after whom the cardiovascular unit at the John Radcliffe is named. However, it is a general medical ward rather than a cardiology one. The other possibility is that it should really be called 'Alexandra Ward' as there was one with this name at the Radcliffe Infirmary. Maybe in the move up to the John Radcliffe Hospital, the name was mistakenly changed.

First of all, a little about Earl Alexander. Harold Rupert Leofric George Alexander was born in London on 10 December 1891. He attended Sandhurst and served with distinction in both world wars. From 1946 to 1952 he was Governor General of Canada.

Whilst in Canada he had a minor heart attack, so when the British Heart Foundation was formed in 1961, he was asked to be the first president. The foundation established its first Chair of Cardiovascular Medicine in Oxford, and the inauguration was a splendid ceremony on 13 October 1973. The Queen Mother unveiled a bust of the Field Marshal (which now resides on Level 6 of the West Wing). The ceremony was attended by university figures as well as by show business celebrities who had helped with fund-raising, including Vera Lynn and Morecambe and Wise. The first holder of the chair was Professor Peter Sleight.

Earl Alexander died on 16 June 1969 following a heart attack. He was seventy-seven years old.

Princess Alexandra (1844–1925)

Whether or not Alexander Ward is named after her, the story of how Alexandra Ward at the Radcliffe Infirmary was named is worth telling. In the 1870s a new wing was opened at the Radcliffe Infirmary. A ceremonial opening was planned for Saturday, 2 June 1877, by Queen Victoria's son Prince Leopold, Duke of Albany. Leopold was the only one of Queen Victoria's sons to suffer from haemophilia, the disorder of blood clotting that ran in the royal families of Europe. He was advised in an article in the *British Medical Journal*, when he suffered a haemorrhage in his knee, to pursue a quiet life, unlike the antics of his racy brother, Edward Prince of Wales. Leopold followed this advice.

Leopold was a Radcliffe Trustee. When the time for the opening of the new wards drew near, there were a number of cases of scarlet fever in the Radcliffe Infirmary. Whilst Doctor Acland, the Regius Professor, was not concerned for Leopold's safety, Sir William Jenner, the royal physician, was not happy, so the meeting took place at the University Museum. It was a grand affair and many notable personages were present. The Prince was updated on the state of the Radcliffe Infirmary. He then asked if the two new women's wards could be named after his mother, Queen Victoria, and his sister-in-law, Princess Alexandra. The latter was the wife of his eldest brother, Edward Prince of Wales, who became King Edward VII in 1901 following the death of Queen Victoria. This was duly done. (Sadly Leopold died in 1884 at Cannes when he fell and hit his head and presumably died of a cerebral haemorrhage at the age of only thirty.)

Queen Alexandra had been born in 1844, to the future King and Queen of Denmark. She married Edward Prince of Wales in 1863 when she was only nineteen. She was considered a great beauty and set the trends in fashion. She had three sons and three daughters, but one son died at only one day old. The eldest son, Albert, died of influenza, so it was his brother George who eventually came to the throne (as King

George V).

Although early in the marriage Alexandra was part of the fashionable social scene, she gradually withdrew from society and spent most of her time at Sandringham. This was partly because of the peccadilloes of her husband, although she was amazingly tolerant and always loved him, and partly because of increasing deafness due to otosclerosis. She worked hard for charity, in particular for nursing. Queen Alexandra's Royal Army Nursing Corps was founded during the Boer War. There was an Alexandra Rose Day every year, when artificial roses made by the disabled were sold by women in aid of hospitals.

King Edward VII died in 1910, but Alexandra lived on until 1925, when she suffered a heart attack. She is buried next to her husband in St George's Chapel, Windsor.

Arthur Sanctuary (1891–1992)

Arthur Sanctuary was administrator of the Radcliffe Infirmary from 1921 to 1951. He saw the medical services in Oxford through a great deal of change. There is a building named after him at the John Radcliffe Hospital which now provides accommodation primarily for Radcliffe Trust employees. It was previously the nursing quarters.

Arthur had a degree from Cambridge University. He was a skilled administrator, who possessed charm and tact but also firmness of character. This stood him in good stead in a post whose function is to enable the many different people working in a hospital to perform their duties to the best of their abilities. He enjoyed the confidence of the lay and medical staff as well as that of the various committees involved in running the hospital. He helped make the Radcliffe Infirmary a happy place to work.

There were enormous changes during the thirty years of his tenure, not least the Nuffield Benefactions, the coming of the National Health Service, and the opening of three new hospitals. When he came to Oxford, there were two hundred and fourteen beds at the Radcliffe Infirmary and the annual expenditure was some £35,000. By the time he retired, there were four additional hospitals to administer, and he was responsible for 1,260 beds and an annual expenditure of over a million pounds. Another important achievement was the changeover from honorary to salaried status of the consultant staff, a difficult task which he carried out with his usual aplomb.

Arthur thus played a very important part in the evolution of medical services in Oxford. He also trained many administrators who went on to hold top positions elsewhere. He wrote a short history of the Radcliffe Infirmary 1921–1948.

He was married to Evelyn and initially they lived in lodgings in the High where they entertained colleagues with lavish dinners. These were legendary, rivalling college high table. Dishes such as cold fillet of sole garnished with lobster were remembered many years later.

From 1926 to 1932 they lived in Manor Farm in Headington. Then they moved into a house that was built especially for the administrator nearby. It was a fine Art Deco house with a handsome carved stone fireplace and it featured in the *Ideal Home* magazine in 1931. Sadly the house was later gutted and used as a Trade Union office, but with the opening of the John Radcliffe Hospital, it became William Osler House, the medical students' club.

Arthur lived to the age of a hundred, dying in 1992. By 1985 his eyesight was very poor. His memories went back a long way. In December 1985 he wrote to Doctor Robb-Smith recalling the opening of the Osler Pavilion on 1 January 1927. (This was a tuberculosis sanatorium built on the Manor House Estate which had been planned by Sir William Osler but not finished until after his death.) Sanctuary wrote: 'I remember quite clearly standing about in the Manor House Drive waiting for Neville Chamberlain to arrive to open the Osler Pavilion—rather a dreary occasion.'

Sir Hugh Cairns (1896–1952)

The medical library at the John Radcliffe Hospital is named after Sir Hugh Cairns, who was the first Nuffield Professor of Surgery. He was in a large part responsible for setting up the clinical medical school in Oxford and was a pioneer of the specialty of neurosurgery in this country. There is also a Hugh Cairns Surgical Society, which encourages and supports Oxford medical students considering a career in surgery as well as raising funds to pay for a student from overseas to visit Oxford on a surgical attachment.

Hugh Cairns was born on 26 June 1896 in South Australia. His father, a Scot, had emigrated there for the climate, because of chest problems. He was a carpenter and joiner and Cairns's mother was a music teacher, who instilled in him a love of music. Hugh won a Government Medical Bursary to the University of Adelaide and began his medical training in 1912 at the age of only fifteen and a half (he was not much older than John Radcliffe had been!). He obtained first class honours in most examinations as well as excelling at sport.

With the outbreak of the First World War in 1914, Cairns interrupted the fourth year of his course to join the Australian Army Medical Corps (AAMC), in which he enlisted as a private in May 1915. He worked as an orderly in the X-ray department of a hospital set up on the Mediterranean island of Lemnos, which provided medical support for the campaign in the Dardanelles and the Gallipoli

Peninsula. Cairns was invalided home with typhoid in the Spring of 1916 and resumed the fourth year of his medical training. That November, he was awarded a Rhodes Scholarship, and qualified in June 1917 after which he was appointed Captain in the AAMC. He sailed to England and reached the frontline in France in April 1918, where he served until the war ended.

In January 1919 Cairns arrived in Oxford to take up his Rhodes Scholarship at Balliol College. He was to meet some of the people who had a major influence on his life and career, in particular Sherrington (Professor of Physiology), Osler, and Cushing. He attended various classes in anatomy and physiology and Osler's ward-rounds. However, after the rigours of the war, he also enjoyed the social life of an Oxford bustling with students of all ages. He rowed for Oxford in 1920. He fell in love with Barbara Smith, youngest daughter of the Master of Balliol, whom he was to marry in November 1921.

Cairns began working as house surgeon at the Radcliffe Infirmary in October 1920, then at the London Hospital in March 1921. Over the next five years, he held various surgical posts at the London, until, in 1926, an opportunity arose that had a great effect on him and on the field of neurosurgery in this country. He was awarded a Rockefeller Travelling Scholarship, and chose to work as assistant resident surgeon to Harvey Cushing at the Peter Bent Brigham Hospital in Boston. Cushing was a pioneer in the field of neurosurgery, and Cairns had met him on a number of occasions in Oxford. Cairns was interested in neurology and the new specialty of neurosurgery so saw this as an ideal opportunity. During this year he learned a huge amount from Cushing, who was a brilliant surgeon, though he could be difficult to work for (and to play tennis with, as he was prone to cheat!).

When Cairns arrived home in September 1927 he wanted, with the support of Cushing and the Rockefeller Foundation, to set up a neurosurgical unit in London. This was not easy because of opposition in the teaching hospitals to specialisation, and also the need for beds, equipment, and specialist staff. It did not materialise for a while either at the London or at Queen's Square, where he also worked from 1931. However, in 1933 he was put in charge of a limited new department of neurosurgery at the London Hospital.

By 1935 he was beginning to think about setting up a unit in Oxford and about the future of medical education there. He worked with Sir Farquhar Buzzard, the Regius Professor of Medicine, and other medical figures and came up with a plan for a clinical course leading to a BM BCh, a graduate scheme for teaching and research, and an eight-year resident training programme. The estimated cost was £1.2 million and Lord Nuffield (see section on Nuffield Orthopaedic Centre) had indicated he was willing to provide money. There were intense negotiations over the summer of 1936 in which Cairns played a key role. The result was a gift of £1.25 million from Lord Nuffield, with the possibility of another million. The 'undergraduate' clinical school did not materialise at this stage. Cairns suggested the new chairs be called Nuffield Professorships. His name was put forward for the first Chair of Surgery, and he was appointed in January 1937 and sworn in as a fellow of Balliol. The family moved to Charlbury Road in North Oxford and Cairns could be seen cycling to work at the Radcliffe Infirmary.

New wards were planned and 'Nuffield I' with twenty-one beds was earmarked for neurosurgery. The unit opened in 1938 and Cairns was ably assisted by Joe Pennybacker who had been his assistant at the London. Lord Nuffield remarked that 'it was Mr Hugh Cairns who had been the first germ of the gift of two million pounds to Oxford for Medicine.' Over the next two years the new department was a busy and successful one. In the year 1938–9, one hundred and fifty-eight operations were performed. Cairns gave jobs to exiles from the Spanish Civil War and later to refugees from Austria and Germany.

At the beginning of the war, with the fear that London would be bombed, it seemed a good opportunity to start a clinical course at the Radcliffe Infirmary and Cairns played an important part in this. In October 1939 the Radcliffe Infirmary clinical school opened with sixty students.

With the beginning of the Second World War in 1939, Cairns was involved in preparations for medical services and was placed in charge of army neurosurgery. He saw the need for a military hospital specialising in head injuries, and saw Oxford as the ideal location: it was within easy reach of London, was unlikely to be bombed, and had Cairns and his team at hand. The facilities were available as most undergraduates were away from Oxford. He chose St Hugh's College for the hospital as women's colleges with corridors rather than staircases were more suitable. So, in February 1940 the Military Hospital for Head Injuries, Oxford, opened. It dealt with all aspects of head injuries, from surgery to rehabilitation. Doctor Ritchie Russell (see later) was the neurologist. It became a training school for a whole generation of neurosurgeons and neurologists. From February 1940 to the end of 1944, the unit treated well over ten thousand patients. At the end of the war it moved to the Churchill Hospital and thence to Wheatley. Cairns was initially an acting Colonel (and Brigadier from 1942).

Another of Cairns's important contributions to the war was the setting up of Mobile Neurosurgical Units (MNSUs). He realised that head injury patients could best be treated by a specialist neurosurgeon within a few hours of injury. These units consisted of a small team including a neurosurgeon, neurologist, anaesthetist, and nursing sister. The units had special equipment including lighting, diathermy, and suction. All were housed in specialised vehicles and contained enough equipment for over two hundred operations. They were sent to various parts, but were especially important in North Africa.

Cairns's third important contribution to the war was his involvement in trials of penicillin among the wounded. He worked closely with Sir Howard Florey, Professor of Pathology and fellow Rhodes Scholar from Australia, who had developed use of penicillin at home. He had shown it was successful given systemically but the problem of short supply was a barrier to its use among battlefield casualties. So Cairns and Florey travelled to North Africa in April 1943 to study results of administering it locally as a powder, cream, or solution. For soft tissue wounds, for example, after surgical excision and cleaning, up to five small rubber tubes were inserted then the wound was sutured. Penicillin solution was injected down the tubes every twelve hours. Results were good and the realisation of the immense importance of penicillin (not least for allowing rapid return of soldiers to action) dawned on the military and the medical profession.

One of Cairns's leading campaigns throughout his career was for the introduction of crash helmets for motorcyclists. In May 1935 he was called in, with Sir Farquhar Buzzard, to give an opinion when Lawrence of Arabia (T. E. Lawrence) had a motorcycle accident near his home in Dorset. He suffered head injury, and died a few days later. Later, during the war, Cairns treated a large number of army dispatch motorcyclists with head injuries and analysed the site and nature of the brain injuries, enabling the scientific design of a crash helmet. Wearing of such a helmet became compulsory in the military in 1941. He continued his campaign for civilian riders after the war though wearing a helmet did not become compulsory until after his death.

Cairns was also involved in setting up the Accident Service at the Radcliffe Infirmary which opened in 1941, the first one in the country. This allowed serious injuries to be admitted directly to an accident ward where different specialists could treat them, with orthopaedic surgeons in administrative charge, and with a neurosurgical registrar attached.

In December 1945, Cairns was flown over to Heidelberg to give an opinion on General George Patton, formerly Commander of the US Third Army, who broke his neck in a motor accident following a pheasant shoot. Sadly he died soon after. (Another famous patient had been Unity Mitford, who in January 1940 had been admitted to the Radcliffe Infirmary following her self-inflicted bullet wound to the brain.)

The future of the medical school was still under discussion during and after the war. Cairns hoped for an academic, research-based undergraduate clinical school leading to working for the Nuffield departments. In fact, the undergraduate clinical school declined with lack of funding and the changes in practice with the coming of the National Health Service. However it survived, largely due to the hard work and dedication of Cairns, and opened its door to five students in 1948. Sir Douglas Veale, the university registrar with whom Cairns worked closely, said that Cairns was 'the person above all others concerned with framing the policy of the Oxford School'. In June 1946, Cairns was appointed a KBE.

Throughout his working life, Cairns published a large number of papers on many subjects. In addition to those already discussed, perhaps his work on tuberculosis should be mentioned. The discovery in the late 1940s that the tubercle bacterium was susceptible to streptomycin was a huge advance for treatment of tuberculous meningitis, for which treatment was previously restricted to surgery in severe cases. In 1950 he travelled widely in America lecturing on the use of streptomycin with tuberculin in treating the disease. In 1951 he visited Africa where he studied the enormity of the problem and difficulties of treatment there as well as the response to the new drugs. (At 13 Norham Gardens we have Cairns's notebook from his trip to Uganda.)

His research was meticulous. He followed in the footsteps of Osler and Cushing, correlating clinical, radiological, and pathological findings. He stressed the importance of accurate record keeping, and also employed two medical artists in Oxford (who were based in one of the Observatory buildings with their dachshunds!).

We are fortunate to have, in the Cairns Library, facsimiles of two case histories of patients cared for by Cushing and Cairns in 1927 in Boston. They illustrate how different neurosurgery was before the days of CT scans. One patient, a Captain Gheradi of the United States Navy, complained of headache, and difficulties with vision and speech. He complained that he could not see to the right. His wife said he had been irritable for three years and also suffered from lack of attention and concentration. He was described by Cairns as 'a magnificently built man of about 6′2″ inclined a little to stoutness'. Examination revealed papilloedema and right homonymous hemianopsia. X-rays showed a shadow on the inner table of the posterior part of the left parietal bone and Cairns made a diagnosis of meningioma of the left posterior parietal region. At surgery a large 170 gram occipital meningioma was found and removed by Cushing. Cairns's history and examination were meticulous as were Cushing's operative notes. The post-operative course was stormy but the patient was discharged a month later. Sadly, we do not know the final outcome. In the operation, diathermy was used to stem bleeding. This had been introduced by Cushing in 1926: prior to this, haemostasis had been achieved by the use of silver clips or by application of pieces of beaten muscle.

Cairns had a happy family life. There were four children and the house in Charlbury Road was busy and bustling with friends and colleagues from all over the world, akin to the Oslers' 'Open Arms' in Norham Gardens. His greatness lay in his ability to concentrate on a number of projects at once, a good memory, and a capacity for hard work. He never wasted a moment. He was an administrative genius and a driven man, full of ideas and with the determination to bring them to fruition. He was a perfectionist and demanded the best from those who worked for him. He was kind to his patients and a zealot in the Hippocratic tradition of passing on his knowledge to his trainees.

Sir Hugh died of lymphosarcoma at the age of only fifty-six, on 18 July 1952. The funeral took place at the University Church in Oxford, followed by memorial services in Oxford and at the London Hospital. He is buried in the churchyard of St Cross Church in Oxford, the church in which he and Barbara were married.

Professor Ritchie Russell (1903–1980)

The Russell Cairns Unit on Level 3 of the West Wing at the John Radcliffe Hospital is named after neurologist Professor Ritchie Russell and neurosurgeon Sir Hugh Cairns (see earlier). The two men worked together in Oxford both during and after the Second World War. The unit is part of the trust's clinical psychology service, whose work includes assessing and treating adults and children with neuropsychological problems following injury to or disease of the brain.

William Ritchie Russell was born in Edinburgh on 7 February 1903, son of a professor of medicine there. Ritchie was educated at Edinburgh Academy then read medicine at Edinburgh University, graduating in 1926. He became interested in neurology early on and after doing his house jobs at the Royal Infirmary, Edinburgh he became resident medical officer at the Hospital for Nervous Diseases, Queen's Square, in London. He was appointed assistant physician at the Royal Infirmary, Edinburgh in 1934 then in 1938 he was appointed lecturer in neurology at the university.

During the Second World War, Russell served in the Royal Army Medical Corps where he rose to the rank of Brigadier. In 1940 he came to Oxford to work with neurosurgeon Hugh Cairns at the Military Hospital for Head Injuries at St Hugh's College. Russell was the officer in charge of the medical division. This became a world-renowned centre, producing many future leaders in the field. Ritchie Russell was later appointed honorary consultant neurologist to the Middle East Forces.

Russell remained in Oxford after the war. Cairns was influential in his appointment as consultant neurologist to the United Oxford Hospitals. This post was set up with a grant from the Nuffield Provincial Hospitals Trust. When he first became consultant, his role was to supervise patients at Stoke Mandeville Hospital, a Ministry of Pensions hospital near Aylesbury, as well as to teach in the university. He did not have any beds at the Radcliffe Infirmary, and indeed his department there consisted of a filing cabinet in a busy corridor. Over the next twenty years he transformed the department of neurology into one of the largest and most prestigious in the country. He moved the inpatient unit from Stoke Mandeville to the Churchill Hospital in Oxford where facilities were excellent. Many postgraduates sought to work in the department, leading to a host of publications and research achievements. The department was later moved to the Radcliffe Infirmary.

In 1949, Russell was appointed lecturer in clinical neurology to the university. Then, in 1966, he was made the first Professor of Clinical Neurology at Oxford, the chair endowed by the National Fund for Research into Poliomyelitis and Other Crippling Diseases. He had many research interests and made many important and original contributions to the field of clinical neurology.

One of his most important was a large follow-up study of over ten thousand men who had suffered penetrating head injuries during the war. His personal card index of patients treated at the Hospital for Head Injuries in Oxford during the war was legendary. He was meticulous in collecting data but equally careful in his concern for and interest in the patients. It led to many papers on cerebral localisation, correlating the site of brain injury with neurological defect, such as aphasia and visual field defects. He was also interested in post-traumatic and retrograde amnesia.

A major interest was care of patients with poliomyelitis. It is hard for us to understand now in what fear this paralysing illness was held. Russell set up a respiratory unit adjacent to the neurology wards. Care was shared with anaesthetists and it was a place of optimism and hope where severely paralysed patients were helped to return to life in the outside world. In 1952 Russell wrote an excellent book, *Poliomyelitis*, covering all aspects of the disease. The polio virus is an enterovirus which attacks motor neurones. Epidemics occurred typically in late summer and early autumn in temperate regions. Following a prodromal illness typically with fever, sore throat, and headache, a few went on to develop paralysis of lower motor neurone type, ranging from a few muscles to complete paralysis including the respiratory muscles. When the brainstem was involved (bulbar poliomyelitis), the muscles of the pharynx, larynx, and palate were affected. Nursing in a prone position with the end of the bed raised coupled with suction may suffice. However, intermittent positive pressure ventilation with tracheostomy may be required and Russell pioneered its use in this country. Those in whom the respiratory muscles are affected may have to be treated in a respirator ('iron lung') which by changes in pressure effects movement of the chest wall. Some few were destined to spend the rest of their lives in a respirator, and benefitted from the special care Russell's multidisciplinary unit provided. Those less severely affected were helped by physiotherapy and sometimes by orthopaedic surgeons to maximise the use of paralysed muscles and deal with the joint deformities resulting. We only need look at the life of Dame Rosemary Rue to see how devastating the disease could be (see section on Churchill Hospital).

The 1956 edition of Russell's book ends on a note of hope, as vaccination was just around the corner. There were two types being tested: Sabin's live attenuated virus given orally (now the standard method in most countries, given as drops on a sugar lump), and Salk's inactivated virus which was given by intramuscular injection. These were one of the major advances of the twentieth century.

Ritchie worked hard to improve the lot of the severely disabled and their carers. This included practical labour-saving devices as well as revising nursing practices. One of his most important projects was the founding of the Young Disabled Unit in Oxford. It was at the Churchill Hospital and was called 'Ritchie Russell House'. It is now part of the

Oxford Centre for Enablement (OCE) at the Nuffield Orthopaedic Centre.

Ritchie was editor of *The Journal of Neurology, Neurosurgery and Psychiatry* for over twenty years.

He retired in 1970, but his interest in neurology went on. He was always adept at fund-raising and he was instrumental in the building of a block of flats in Summertown, Oxford, particularly aimed at providing dignified care for the elderly. It was called 'Ritchie Court' and he lived there himself when not in his house in the south of France.

Whilst quiet and serious in manner, he was adept at Scottish dancing. Indeed, some thought his work was like his dancing: done with perfect timing and seemingly little effort, but completed to perfection. He was a keen member of the euthanasia society, Exit.

Ritchie died on 8 December 1980 aged seventy-seven. In 1932 he had married Jean and they had a son, who became a doctor, and a daughter.

Sir George Pickering (1904–1980)

Sir George Pickering was Regius Professor of Medicine at Oxford from 1956 to 1968. The Medical Education Centre in the academic block at the John Radcliffe Hospital is named after him, which is fitting as he took a great interest in medical education. He revolutionised the medical school at Oxford and is also remembered as a great clinical scientist especially for his work on hypertension.

George White Pickering was born in Whalton, a village in Northumberland, on 26 June 1904. He came from a farming family, but sadly his father who was a teacher died when George was young. His mother educated George and his sister herself, then Sir George went to Newcastle Grammar School where he excelled. Wanting to spread his wings, George asked to be sent away to school, and moved to Dulwich College to complete his schooling.

He gained a scholarship to study natural science at Pembroke College, Cambridge, going up in 1923. He had originally intended to read agricultural science, but a friend had persuaded him to read natural science. Here began his interest in physiology. He gained a double first. Whilst at Cambridge, he met fellow medical student Carola Seward, who was daughter of the Professor of Botany and Master of Downing. They were married in 1930 and had a son and three daughters.

In 1926, having decided to study medicine, he won a scholarship to

St Thomas's. He supplemented his income by teaching biology at Westminster School. He began to attend ward rounds at University College Hospital which was a centre for the developing discipline of 'clinical science', the scientific study of clinical problems. It was championed by Sir Thomas Lewis, who had a great influence on Pickering.

Pickering qualified in 1928 and soon moved to University College to work under Lewis as assistant in the department of clinical research and lecturer in cardiovascular pathology. It was a stimulating environment with a host of brilliant minds, and Pickering worked there for eight years. He was highly regarded by Lewis who encouraged his spirit of enquiry. His work there included research into headache, peptic ulcers, and temperature regulation. However, his most important research was in the field of control of the circulation and hypertension. In 1931 he was appointed to the permanent scientific staff of the Medical Research Council.

In 1939 he moved to St Mary's Hospital Medical School as Professor of Medicine, having come to the notice of Sir Charles Wilson (later Lord Moran, physician to Churchill and saviour of St Mary's Medical School). During the war, the medical school was moved out of London, but on its return at the end of the war, it went from strength to strength. Despite having to work in a small converted shop in Praed Street, medics from all over the world came to work with Pickering both at the bedside and in the laboratory, lapping up the atmosphere of excitement and critical enquiry.

Among other topics, he developed his interest in fever, and a body-temperature research unit was set up by the MRC. He was involved in searching for a pyrogen that was responsible for fever in medical disorders, and caused fever experimentally. His work on the circulation and hypertension continued.

In 1956, Sir George was appointed Regius Professor of Medicine at Oxford at a time when the role was changing. In the past, for example the days of Osler and Garrod (both of whom Pickering greatly admired), little formal teaching was required and both Regii had already achieved their life's work. The post was seen as something of a sinecure. The clinical school, which had originally opened during the war for students from London, was expanding and the Radcliffe Infirmary was a busy teaching hospital. The coming of the National Health Service had brought changes too. Pickering was the first Regius Professor to be a clinician actively in charge of beds. Pickering stated he would only accept the chair if facilities for the Regius improved. So, with the aid of the Wellcome Trust a new university clinical department was formed for the Regius Professor, laboratories being built above the children's wards, and the beds of Doctor Hobson being taken over on his retirement. (There was a great deal of difficulty over this as new departments were built for the Nuffield departments of medicine and surgery as well, and the spending exceeded that agreed by the Department of Health, so that a House of Commons committee held an investigation).

The situation was complex when Sir George arrived in Oxford, with different factions competing. Thus relations between the university and the academic staff on the one hand, and the board of governors of the hospital representing the service needs of the hospital on the other were strained. There was also conflict between full-time and part-time teachers and between the supporters of undergraduate and postgraduate teaching. Pickering steered a course through this quagmire and played a vital role in the further development of the clinical school.

It had opened at the beginning of the war, catering for medical students from London as well as from Oxford. The Goodenough Committee of 1944 had supported the idea of a new experimental type of medical school at Oxford. It was fully developed in 1946 but with an intake of only five students. However, it struggled and nobody really wanted to do their clinical training in Oxford. When Pickering arrived in 1956 he did not like what he saw, and with his usual enthusiasm and drive, set about improving the course. It was he, with the help of Professor Beeson (who came from Yale—see later) who completely transformed the medical school. It was a place people wanted to come to, and numbers increased to a hundred a year. Pickering encouraged the director of clinical studies to improve the curriculum and encouraged students from Cambridge (which had no clinical school) as well as other medical schools to apply. He travelled round Britain, campaigning for the Oxford school. He was, however, focusing on training of doctors to become consultants or go in to research, and only reluctantly accepted the inclusion of a spell in general practice in the clinical course.

As well as producing a first-class medical school, Sir George sought to run a first-class department too. He attracted research workers from all over the world and many important publications stemmed from his team. There was an air of excitement and morale was high. One of his department's interests now was the role of baroreceptors in blood pressure control which he had researched previously. Another was vascular wall disease and the role of fibrin deposition, which he believed to be the source of platelet emboli. He continued his work on fever and on hypertension and his team also studied survival in extreme conditions.

Sir George encouraged research by NHS consultants, to take away the division between service and university positions. So funds were made available for research facilities for consultants, termed 'University Lecturers', who had part of their salary paid by the university, instead of doing private practice. He didn't think much of surgeons. When patients with an upper gastrointestinal bleed were admitted under his care, he was against referring them for surgery. Instead he transfused huge numbers of units of blood, sometimes as many as eighty or ninety. This made him unpopular with the blood transfusion service and put his students and housemen in a difficult position.

As far as Pickering's scientific career is concerned, his most important work was in the field of the arterial circulation and hypertension. In 1936 he started his experimental work on hypertension. He will be remembered for 'rediscovering' renin, the enzyme produced by the kidney which leads to the formation of angiotensin I and II. These cause vasoconstriction, so maintaining blood pressure. Goldblatt in 1934 had demonstrated that clipping the renal artery in the rabbit produced hypertension. Pickering suspected a blood-borne vasoconstrictor, and with Prinzmetal in 1938 was able to extract renin from normal rabbit kidneys. Infusing it into conscious rabbits caused a rise in blood pressure. Renin had first been discovered in 1898 by Tigerstedt and Bergman but 'forgotten' until these studies.

In the late 1940s, Pickering became interested in hypertension in man again, especially the relation between genetic and environmental factors. His work was an important contribution to the field. He set about ascertaining whether essential hypertension was inherited as a Mendelian dominant, a view espoused by Professor (later Lord) Platt. Platt believed that patients with essential hypertension were a separate group, but Pickering believed that blood pressure showed a normal distribution, so that those with high blood pressure were merely the upper end of this normal distribution. He stressed the danger of choosing an arbitrary figure above which the individual was considered hypertensive or 'ill'. The public debate between Pickering and Platt led one reader to complain of their 'blathering, nattering and bickering'.

Another advance was the development of beat-to-beat blood pressure recording via a cannula in the brachial artery. The pressure was recorded during various conditions such as driving round a racing track. In 1955 he published a scholarly five-hundred page tome entitled *High Blood Pressure*, which soon became a classic. It is an exhaustive study of the whole field of blood pressure and hypertension.

Education was a life-long interest and something Sir George felt passionately about. As long ago as 1940 he was secretary of the Royal College of Physicians' Committee on Medical Education. The 1961 Christ Church Conference led to the beginnings of postgraduate and continuing education in medicine. It was, however, the Pembroke Conference of 1973 organised by the Nuffield Provincial Hospitals Trust that led to important changes. A survey was commissioned to look at undergraduate, postgraduate, and continuing medical education, and the findings were published by Pickering in his report 'Quest for Excellence in Medical Education' in 1978. He addressed the problems of the breadth of the undergraduate course requiring the acquisition of facts rather than the training of the mind. He deplored examination by multiple choice. His conclusion was the fear that students and young doctors are being put in a straitjacket with the aim of eliminating bad doctors, but at the same time eliminating the best.

This report echoed the views expressed in his famous President's Address to the annual meeting of the British Medical Association in 1963. It was entitled 'Manners Makyth Man, a plea for the importance of character in medicine'. He took the title from the motto of William of Wyckham, founder of Winchester College and of New College, Oxford. In it he expressed his fears that the ethos of medicine, the role of the doctor in alleviating suffering, is in danger of being lost to the increasing place of science and to the growth of specialism. Both selection of medical students, and progress through training, are so dependent upon exam success that the character and humanity of the doctor takes second place.

One of Pickering's most important contributions to medicine was the setting up of postgraduate medical centres. In 1964 he arranged a meeting where the establishment of these centres and of postgraduate tutors in both teaching hospitals and district general hospitals was discussed. Through his influence they have proliferated and are now established and greatly appreciated institutions, important for the intellectual and social needs of doctors in the area, not least GPs. Another important achievement was the part he played in the setting up of the new medical schools at Nottingham and Southampton.

Sir George received many accolades during his life and held many important positions in the university. He received his knighthood in 1957 and was elected a Fellow of the Royal Society in 1960 in recognition of his contribution to the scientific basis of medicine. On retirement as Regius Professor in 1968, Sir George became Master of Pembroke College, Oxford. He finally retired in 1974.

In an interesting digression from his writings on clinical science and education, in 1974 Pickering made a foray into psychology and published a book entitled *Creative Malady*. He studied the role of illness in the lives and accomplishments of six eminent Victorians from the worlds of science and the arts. The idea for the book stemmed from his personal experience. He noted how, when confined to bed because the pain from the osteoarthritis of his hips was so severe, he had time to contemplate and work, free from the myriad demands on a Regius

Professor. Indeed, after his hip replacements, he missed his 'old friend'. One of his subjects was Charles Darwin, and Pickering made a detailed study of his life and writings and noted how while previously an energetic and fit man, a year after the return from his voyage on the *Beagle*, he became increasingly unwell and before long a recluse. Pickering proposed that this was a psychological illness, which allowed him to concentrate on his life's work, free from the distractions of society. He believed it to be the result of an inner conflict, resolved by the protective mechanism of illness.

Sir George was an eccentric character by all accounts. He was a short man with a mischievous, impish air. Enthusiasm was his watchword, and he approached life with gusto. The medical students were devoted to him, and women found him charming.

If you were one of 'Pickering's boys' your career was made, but if he didn't like you, things were not so good. He had the ability to recognize talent, then inspire and stimulate you to achieve. People who worked for him in London or Oxford went on to fill prestigious posts in Britain and abroad. He inspired great loyalty and people travelled from great distances to attend his funeral.

Sir George held strong views on all sorts of subjects. For example he had great antipathy to those he called the 'salt evangelists' who believed there was a strong correlation between salt intake and blood pressure.

He had hesitant speech and a diffident manner as well as a benign essential tremor. On one famous occasion he decided to demonstrate how to do a lumbar puncture to his students and junior doctors, one of them having failed. All was made ready, it was a moment of pure theatre. But Pickering was hampered by the tremor, and he failed. The story goes that the patient exclaimed, 'Will someone take that bloody woodpecker off my back!'

He owned an ancient pre-war car but was usually to be seen cycling. He gained pleasure from leaning his bike against one of the Rolls Royces parked outside the Radcliffe Infirmary. He was untidy-looking, failing to notice that his shirt was tattered. In the 1956 'Tyngewick' production, the newly-appointed Pickering was portrayed by the medical students as Professor Kippering, a man who measured everything. He was kind to patients though, showing great humanity and understanding. His interests outside medicine included gardening and fishing, both stemming from his days in the Northumbrian countryside. He was proud of his county of birth and was known to entertain international conferences with Tyneside songs.

Sir George and Lady Carola were the first Regius Professor and wife to live at 13 Norham Gardens since Grace Osler had left the house for the use of the Regius Professor of Medicine in 1928. This was fitting as Sir George was such a great admirer of Osler.

He died on 3 September 1980 aged seventy-six, following a stroke and pneumonia. He is buried in the extension to the burial ground in Ewelme, the village south of Oxford where the Regius Professor is Master of the Almshouses. Like Osler before him, he took great interest in the care of the residents. Sir George had always shown great interest in the Osler House Boat Club, and on his death, his old friends and colleagues contributed to the purchase of a new boat bearing his name.

All in all, he was a man of great enthusiasm and intelligence who was largely responsible for creating a world-class medical school at Oxford.

Professor Paul Beeson (1908–2006)

The Beeson Room in the Cairns Library at the John Radcliffe Hospital is named after Paul Beeson, Nuffield Professor of Medicine at Oxford from1965 to 1974. He was an American clinician, teacher, and scientist who was at the forefront of research into infectious disease, fever, and immunology.

Paul Bruce Beeson was born in rural Montana on 18 October 1908. His father John was a doctor who had set up in general practice. This involved a wide range of skills including medicine, surgery, orthopaedics, and obstetrics. John's main influence was Sir William Osler (see earlier), whose *Principles and Practice of Medicine* had been published in 1892. Paul's mother was a teacher. His grandfather on his father's side had fought in the Civil War on the side of the Union.

The family moved to Seattle in 1915 but there was not enough work so they went to live in Alaska which was a bustling place with the building of the Alaska railroad. It was frontier land and cold. In winter, the family pet dog would take Paul to school on a sledge. Paul did well at the local primary school and in 1925 graduated from Anchorage High School. It was the time of the Depression. He went to the University of Washington, initially to read business administration. He enjoyed life as a student, playing sports and attending the movies and parties. He changed to medicine and then moved to the University of McGill in Montreal in Canada to study medicine there. He discovered

Sir William Osler's Library, but sadly was frightened off by the librarian W. W. Francis and never went there again. Paul had a 1931 edition of Osler's textbook, which remained the standard text.

On graduation in 1933, Paul's elder brother Harold, who had studied medicine before him, arranged for Paul to begin his postgraduate education with William Pepper at the University of Pennsylvania Hospital. By this time his father and Harold had started a family practice in Wooster, a farming town in Ohio. Paul joined them for two years. However, he soon found that he lacked surgical skill and confidence, and decided that general medicine was the path he wanted to take.

After a short spell at the New York Hospital, he moved to the Rockefeller Institute in New York in 1937. This was a high-powered academic institution and suited him well. He was assistant resident in the pneumonia service. It was an exciting time and it seemed the era of Osler was coming to an end with new scientific discoveries and treatments. Anti-pneumococcal serum, type-specific antibodies produced in horse or rabbit and injected into patients for treatment of pneumonia, had been developed at the Rockefeller Institute in the early 1930s. This was now, however, superseded by the introduction of sulphonamides, the first antibiotics. These heralded a new age where, for the first time, pneumonia could be brought under control. Prior to their introduction, over fifty thousand people died each year in the USA from pneumonia. Paul began his research work here and realised that this was where his future lay. He worked on the immunological similarity between the capsular polysaccharide of type X14 pneumococcus and blood group A.

In 1939 he became chief resident at the Peter Bent Brigham Hospital at Harvard in Boston. Here he continued his research on infectious disease, producing a number of papers on various aspects of pneumonia.

The outbreak of the Second World War in 1939 brought about changes. Beeson was appointed chief physician of the Harvard–Red Cross Field Unit Hospital. The unit, which included a prefabricated wooden building plus nursing and medical staff, was a gift from

Harvard to Britain and was shipped across the Atlantic. It was for the study of epidemiology and for treatment of infectious diseases. This was important because of the fear of epidemics occurring among the soldiers living and working in crowded conditions and also among civilians crowded in air raid shelters. It was opened near Salisbury, in Wiltshire in September 1941 with a hundred and twenty-six beds. It was jointly run by Harvard, the American Red Cross, and the British Ministry of Health. Here Paul began to be noticed as a skilled physician and it was here that he met American nurse Barbara Neal whom he started dating and married in 1942. They had two sons and a daughter.

Once America entered the war after Pearl Harbour in December 1941, the hospital was transferred to the US Army. However, Paul was not eligible for military service because of a chronic health problem, so he returned to America and in 1942 became Assistant Professor of Medicine at Emory Hospital in Atlanta. He showed skill as a teacher and investigator in the field of infectious diseases and immunology. He developed an interest in subacute bacterial endocarditis and also in the reticuloendothelial system (a diffuse system of phagocytic cells important in the immune process). He studied the relationship between fever and white blood cells. He also showed that hepatitis could be transmitted by blood transfusion. In 1946 Beeson was made professor at Emory. He was now an international figure.

In 1952 Beeson became Chief of Medicine and Ensign Professor at Yale, at the New Haven Hospital. He was in and out of hospital himself for six months with medical problems. He was an inspiring and kind teacher, holding parties for his staff (where he was a mean croquet player). He was always ready to help and advise. He made a study of the causes of persistent fever, and it was at Yale that he made what was perhaps his most important scientific discovery: he was the first to identify the proteins called cytokines, chemical messengers important in the immune response.

Beeson had to deal with a huge administrative load at Yale, and felt he needed a break. So in 1958 he took a sabbatical, working in the Wright–Fleming Institute of Microbiology at St Mary's in London; this was at the suggestion of his friend Sir George Pickering (see earlier). It gave Beeson time for basic research without administrative or clinical commitments and also the chance to spend more time with his family. He worked on the complement system, the plasma proteins that through a cascade process activated by antigen–antibody interaction, help fight infection.

He returned home refreshed. His prestige grew across the nation and the term the 'Beeson mystique' was coined. He was described as having an aura of greatness and charm. He was in fact a shy, quiet, and modest man, equally gracious in his dealings with both colleagues and patients. He was a superb clinical teacher, and students and junior doctors alike were inspired to be like him. Despite his outstanding abilities, he was blessed with humility and great compassion. He was considered a leading physician in the world and travelled widely in the US, Canada, and Europe to give lectures.

In 1965, he was recovering from a knee operation when he received a letter from Sir George Pickering, Regius Professor of Medicine at Oxford, asking if would like to be considered for the Chair of Nuffield Professor of Medicine at Oxford. The first professor, Leslie Witts, was retiring. When he came over to look round, Paul could see the advantages as he could spend more time in the lab and on the wards with patients and students, and less time on administration. Pickering saw him as someone who could unite the medical school, both the different clinical 'firms' and the preclinical and clinical schools. So, he was duly appointed at the age of fifty-six. Rather like Osler, Beeson saw it as a godsend.

He and his wife Barbara, together with daughter Judy and dog and cat, moved into a flat in the High Street. There were some teething troubles and it took him a while to get used to the set-up in Oxford, but he had a major role in the teaching of medicine at Oxford. The family moved to Boar's Hill.

One of his major contributions was the introduction of the 'bridge course', a six-month course to introduce medical students to the clinical training. It included clinical pathology, the arts of history-taking, physical examination, and laboratory evaluation. He got generous funding from the Commonwealth Fund and it has survived to this day, albeit with some differences. He brought in more continuous assessment and clinical examinations in the clinical course, rather than the old system of essays. He was a support to Pickering, and played a valuable role in fostering trust and cooperation in the medical school.

Paul also played a role in the founding of Green Templeton College, and indeed, it was he who persuaded Cecil Green, the head of Texas Instruments, to donate the first million dollars for the college. In typically generous fashion, Beeson donated his own college pension for the upkeep of 13 Norham Gardens, home of the Oslers in Oxford.

His research in Oxford included work on eosinophilia and the role of these white blood cells in infection, neoplasia, and allergic conditions. He saw that the field of infectious disease would be revolutionised by genetics, and indeed he went a long way to making Oxford pre-eminent in the specialty of infectious diseases, as it is today.

While in Oxford he co-edited the *Oxford Companion to Medicine*, a popular textbook which became a standard tome for those studying for the MRCP. He was made an Honorary Knight Commander of the British Empire in 1973. He retired two years early, in 1974, so that his successor, Sir David Weatherall, would be in position for the move of the hospital up to the Headington site. So the family (this time with a horse too) flew back to America.

Beeson took up a post as distinguished physician at the Veterans Administration Hospital at the University of Washington in Seattle. The purpose of this scheme was to extend the teaching lives of academics and to support them financially in later life. Treatment was provided free to patients in need. He retired from this post in 1981.

Towards the end of his career, he became interested in the care of the elderly, perhaps influenced by his mother's dementia. He wrote an important paper, 'Quality of Survival', in which he opposed euthanasia and promoted a caring, easy, and dignified path to death. He came to mourn the loss of the generalist in medicine, but he saw it in the care of the elderly and became involved in training health professionals in this field. He promoted a holistic approach, having the right glasses and walking aid being as important as high-tech remedies. He was editor of the *Journal of the American Geriatrics Society* and indeed transformed the image of geriatric medicine in the United States.

He became disillusioned by the capitalism and materialism of the 1980s. Having been a conservative all his life, he became a liberal concerned with free treatment for the elderly and the uninsured. Here he was influenced by the National Health Service in Britain with which he had been impressed. He became an ardent activist, working for Physicians for Social Responsibility, an organisation campaigning against the escalation of the nuclear threat. He travelled widely lecturing. A Paul Beeson Peace Award was founded. In 2002 he and Barbara moved to a retirement community in Exeter, New Hampshire and he died on 14 August 2006 at the age of ninety-seven.

In many ways, his life mirrored that of his hero William Osler whom he would often quote. Both men spent their childhood on the North American frontier, living a simple life before studying medicine at McGill. They were both able clinicians, teachers, and scientists. Beeson carried on in Osler's tradition of humanism in medicine, always showing kindness and gentleness to patients and colleagues. Both gained a great reputation as clinician and teacher and were held in great affection both in North America and in Oxford.

Professor Archibald Cochrane (1909–1988)

The Cochrane Centre at the John Radcliffe Hospital is named after Archibald Cochrane, medical researcher and epidemiologist. He was a pioneer of evidence-based medicine, instituting study of the efficacy of health care by the review of random controlled trials, and making this information available to clinicians. He led an interesting and eventful life, like something from *Boy's Own*.

Archibald Leman Cochrane was born on 12 January 1909 in Galashiels in Scotland to a prosperous family. His father was in the textile business, but was killed in the First World War. Archie was educated at Uppingham School, then in 1927 won a scholarship to read medicine at King's College, Cambridge. He gained a double first. His ambition was to become a don and he started a research project on tissue culture in Cambridge. However, this was not for him and he then went to Berlin as he felt he would benefit from psychoanalysis. He followed his analyst round Europe for two years and developed a hatred of fascism, and also an understanding of the importance of validating all theories by experimentation.

He returned to Britain in 1935 and did his clinical training at University College Hospital in London. Here he was greatly influenced both by Philip D'Arcy Hart's social concern and also by Sir Thomas Lewis and George Pickering's scientific rigour and enthusiasm (see earlier). But before qualifying, he went with the Ambulance Unit of the

International Brigade to support the Republic in the Spanish Civil War, in which his experience included triage on the battlefield.

He returned to University College Hospital and finally qualified. But soon there opened a new chapter in his life. On the outbreak of the Second World War, he joined the Royal Army Medical Corps, serving from 1939 to 1946. After eighteen months he was captured in Crete and found himself a prisoner of war. He eventually became the British officer in charge of prison hospitals, working in prison camps in Greece and Germany. He found time to do research on various topics including famine oedema, and became an expert on tuberculosis.

On demobilisation, he developed his interest in epidemiology and preventive medicine, winning a Rockefeller Fellowship. Following his wartime experience, he specialised in chest diseases. He was a member of the Medical Research Council Pneumoconiosis Research Unit in Penarth in Wales, working under Charles Fletcher. In 1960 he was appointed Professor of Tuberculosis and Chest Diseases in the Welsh National School of Medicine in Cardiff. He became Director of the MRC Epidemiology Research Unit there. He was the first to demonstrate a quantitative correlation between the development of pneumoconiosis and exposure to dust (rather than silica). In 1972 he became the first president of the newly founded Faculty of Community Medicine in Cardiff.

Archibald went on to apply his experience in population studies to a wide range of diseases. He was a major figure in what was then the developing science of epidemiology. He was a meticulous researcher. His most important publication was a book in 1972 entitled *Effectiveness and Efficiency: Random Reflections on Health Services*. Here was a simple but ground-breaking proposition. He argued that in a world where resources are always limited, the medical profession should provide care that had been shown to be effective. He stressed there should be reviews of random controlled trials, the results of which should be easily available to health care professionals. Thus clinicians and medical administrators should base their practice on scientific research studies, rather than on tradition, personal impression, theory, or precept.

In 1979 he published an important essay stressing the value of such critical studies in different specialties and subspecialties. This led to the development in the 1980s of the Oxford Database of Perinatal Trials. The success of this international collaboration was followed by similar studies in other specialties. It led to the opening of the Cochrane Centre at the John Radcliffe Hospital in Oxford in 1992, some four years after Archibald's death, named in his honour. It received support from the Nuffield Provincial Hospitals Trust. The following year the Cochrane Collaboration was founded. It is an international, non-profit making, independent organisation. Its aim is for healthcare decisions throughout the world to be informed by carefully evaluated research evidence. The Collaboration produces and disseminates systematic reviews of healthcare interventions. These 'Collaboration Reviews' are produced electronically and updated regularly. As time has gone by, many specialties have become involved. In 2011 some twenty-eight thousand healthcare professionals were working with the Cochrane Collaboration in over a hundred countries, mostly as volunteers preparing and maintaining the reviews of random controlled trials.

Cochrane was profoundly affected by his experiences with prisoners of war. In one camp in Greece he was the only doctor in a camp of some twenty thousand men. The medical armoury was limited to skin antiseptic, aspirin, and antacids. Despite severe epidemics of diphtheria and typhoid, very few men died. Cochrane was impressed by the ability of the human body to triumph over disease, and the relative unimportance of medical intervention.

In Germany, he looked after a camp where prisoners of war of all nationalities with tuberculosis were sent. There were no X-ray facilities, but there were facilities for analysis of sputum smears and for surgical treatment such as pneumothorax and thoracoplasty. He describes how he came to know his patients well. He would attend the funerals of those who died, often acting as priest. Indeed, he became an expert in Greek Orthodox, Moslem, and Hindu rites. He tells a touching story of a young Russian prisoner of war with tuberculosis being brought screaming to the ward late one night. Cochrane, detecting a pleural rub, believed pleurisy to be the cause of the pain. With no morphine available, he gave him aspirin but to no avail. Finally, loath to wake the other patients, he took the man into his own room and held him in his arms. The crying ceased, and the young man died peacefully a few hours later. Cochrane felt this moving experience was a salutary lesson in the care of the dying.

Despite working long hours, Archibald found time to create a beautiful garden, even opening it to the public under the National Gardens Scheme. He won a Royal Horticultural Society award. He also collected modern art and sculpture and wrote poetry.

He applied his medical knowledge to his family too. His sister was thought to be suffering from dementia, but Archibald thought it might be porphyria. This was the case, and he was found to have it too. Very public-spiritedly, he contacted a hundred and fifty-three members of his family from as far afield as New Zealand, and tested them to see if they had the disease. All but one of those he contacted replied! He was a bachelor. He died of cancer on 18 June 1988 at the age of seventy-nine.

A great one for expounding his latest enthusiasm, Archibald was a good and caring friend and colleague. He was a true eccentric. In a time where we are all aware of the concept of evidence-based medicine, we owe much to his pioneering work which has had a major effect on the practice of medicine worldwide.

Doctor Lionel Cosin (1910–1994)

The Geriatric Day Hospital on Level 4 at the John Radcliffe Hospital is named after a pioneer of geriatric medicine, Lionel Cosin, who was the first to found a day hospital for the elderly. It was the happy marriage of an interest in surgery and in geriatrics that led to a revolution in the care of the elderly.

Lionel Zelick Cosin was born in London on 8 November 1910. His father was an estate agent. He was educated at Westminster City School then went on to study medicine at Guy's, qualifying in 1933. He intended to specialise in surgery and took a job at the Littlemore Hospital in Oxford, hoping he would find time to study for the FRCS. To this end he came armed with twenty years' worth of the *British Journal of Surgery*. Not surprisingly he passed. He planned to work in the neurosurgery department at the London Hospital, but when war came, many of the departments of the London teaching hospitals were moved out to the provinces. So instead he took up a post at the Essex County Council hospital at Orsett in Essex where he was a general surgeon specialising in the treatment of war casualties.

The hospital had three hundred beds for the elderly chronic sick, and when the medical superintendent retired in 1940, Cosin was put in charge of these cases as well as his own surgical patients. This turned out to be a turning point in his career.

When the stream of war casualties ceased in 1944, Cosin had time to ponder on the care of the chronically ill patients under his care. The expectation at that time was that the patients would remain in hospital for the rest of their life. There was no expectation of improvement and no provision for rehabilitation. There were two empty wards at the hospital and this meant that Cosin could admit patients at short notice. Some had a fractured neck of femur and at that time, they would have been considered too old for treatment and would be kept in bed until they died. This is where Cosin's surgical training came in. He operated on these patients; they were rehabilitated and then sent home. This was unheard of previously.

Over the eighteen months leading up to the introduction of the National Health Service in July 1948, Cosin, with the help of a statistician, made a detailed appraisal of length of stay and outcome for his patients at Orsett Hospital. He showed that if elderly patients were managed appropriately early on, with a suitable programme of treatment and rehabilitation, many could return home. Only 17 per cent of his patients needed continuing inpatient hospital care. Of these, some were ambulant but, under the Poor Law, had nowhere to go. This was because the Local Authority was not required to provide care for the elderly other than in hospitals for the infirm and chronically sick. (This changed later when old peoples' homes were organised under the new NHS.) Others required care because of severe physical problems such as stroke or arthritis. Others required help for 'senile dementia', though Cosin believed their problems were often a complex upset in many systems, sometimes due to overuse of medication.

His views were not popular at first, but he was a persuasive man and began to demand attention. He knew how to get his ideas implemented. He presented his results at the Royal Society of Medicine. He later persuaded the Chief Medical Officer to plan for geriatric units within general hospitals in the new NHS, rather than consigning patients to institutions for the chronically ill. His reputation spread and he contributed to a British Medical Association report in 1949 which set out guidelines for a new geriatric service.

Meanwhile, at the first meeting of the board of governors of the Radcliffe Infirmary under the NHS, the future of geriatrics in Oxford was set. Somewhat surprisingly, in the academic world of Oxford with the demands of a fledgling medical school and an increasing number of specialties, geriatrics was given high priority. This view was inspired by Sir Hugh Cairns. Leslie Witts, the Nuffield Professor of Medicine, took responsibility for care of the elderly and asked Sidney Truelove to implement the scheme. He had heard about Cosin's work in Essex, and saw the need for a clinical director of the Cowley Road Hospital with a special interest in care of the elderly. So in May 1950 Lionel Cosin was appointed.

Cosin used his experience at Orsett to good effect. The Cowley Road Hospital was very dilapidated, as the Local Authority was planning its closure and relocation to another site. The patients there remained in bed until they died and when Cosin arrived, 81 per cent of the patients had been bedfast for more than a year. Nobody took any interest in their clinical state. When he arrived, the average length of stay was three hundred days. (Twenty years later, this had fallen to thirty-five days.)

Two pioneering ideas were germinating in Cosin's mind when he came to Oxford, and both came to fruition over the next few years. One was a half-way house, based at Hurdis House, built by the National Corporation for the Care of Old People. Initially the Local Authority financed the patients' treatment, but later the United Oxford Hospitals took over the financial responsibility.

The other innovation and his most important contribution to geriatrics was a day hospital for the elderly. The Cowley Road Day Hospital was the first in the world, opening in 1957. It was adapted by a grant from the Nuffield Provincial Hospitals Trust. The day hospital (a hospital without beds) allowed a multidisciplinary approach, and patients could continue their assessment, medical treatment, and rehabilitation whilst living at home. Cosin's motto was 'bed is bad'.

Whilst he specialised in rehabilitation, Cosin understood the importance of diagnosing and treating physical problems. But he knew that other factors were important too.

He advocated the 'dynamic quadruple assessment'. The primary three assessments are the pathological, the psychological, and the sociological which must be repeated as the patients' condition changes.

The fourth assessment is the most important and is termed the residual physical disability. This determines the nature of any physical rehabilitation required. This quadruple approach allows the multiple problems of the sick elderly patient to be addressed.

The day hospital had close links with the main Cowley Road Hospital, providing opportunity for in- or out-patient treatment. Its aim was to maintain the patient's independence within the community. The team was led by a superintendent occupational therapist. A team consisting of a psychiatrist, a clinician, a medical social worker, and an occupational therapist made decisions about admitting patients to the day hospital. Most patients came after a spell as an inpatient. Others followed referral from the GP, usually following deterioration of the family situation. This might require a domiciliary visit or an outpatient appointment. The programme of activities for the patient could then be planned. Any physiotherapy required was often addressed first. One of the beauties of the system was the informal way in which the patients could be assessed and treated. Thus a patient might be seen by a social worker or doctor in a quiet corner of the dayroom, unlike the much more formal and sometimes intimidating outpatient or ward round consultation. In addition, the repeated attendance allowed longitudinal observations to be made.

Sometimes the admission to hospital followed collapse of the family situation, whose members felt unable to cope. The day hospital played an important role in sharing responsibility with the family once the patient was discharged from the ward. This was very important and might be the deciding factor allowing the patient to remain in the community. It also served to give the family a break. The Medical Officer of Health, Doctor John Warin, campaigned for additional ambulances to transport patients to the day hospital.

At the same time Cosin introduced a 'holiday bed' allowing relatives to take a few weeks' break knowing their family member was being well looked after. He also instituted a 'floating bed' for patients requiring regular treatment but able to live at home most of the time. Cosin's innovations were valuable in two respects. They were very cost-effective, but at the same time they provided optimal care for the patient and their family.

Cosin also opened a forty-bed rehabilitation unit. It consisted of four virtually independent units of ten beds, each with its own rehabilitation team. Ever practical and full of ideas, he planned it bearing in mind an observation he had made in the day hospital. There he had found the benefit of a square corridor which would take the wandering patient nowhere except back to where they started.

He also developed a unit called 'The Warren' in Abingdon. Here elderly married couples came to stay together so that the more fit and active one could be taught new ways of looking after the feebler one. They were then able to return to the community.

An interesting case history illustrates how successful a tailored treatment at the day hospital could be. A sixty-five-year-old man was referred to the day hospital because of depression and deterioration of his personality. This followed a cerebral thrombosis. The man had been a brilliant piano player, but now could not play at all. The referring doctor begged that the patient be given no unrealistic hope that he would play again. The programme of assessment included a physical examination which revealed persistent problems with the left arm and hand. Thus there was some oedema, weakness of the hand muscles, contracture of the fingers, and loss of extension of the fingers.

Treatment began with prolonged immersion of the left hand in paraffin wax on each attendance. He did basket weaving in the craft room which helped to mobilise the left hand. The physiotherapists taught him exercises to strengthen the shoulder, arm, and hand. He began to improve greatly. He became sociable, and chatted to the staff and patients. His depression lifted and he showed pride in his handiwork. His irritability had gone. More to the point, he began to play the piano again. Before starting his practice, he would immerse his hand in paraffin wax using a double saucepan at home. He started with Gilbert and Sullivan, then he tackled the 'Harmonious Blacksmith'. While he knew he would never reach his previous standard, he practised hard to see how good he could get. This case illustrates how a holistic approach, depending on a detailed analysis of the patient's problems, allows an individual programme of treatment which can have dramatic results. It changed this patient's life completely.

Oxford became world renowned in the field of geriatrics and Cosin attracted able doctors from around the world to work with him. It became a centre for teaching and Cosin was in great demand to lecture all over the world, holding several visiting professorships. He advised on geriatric care in a number of countries. He was Clinical Director of the Geriatric Unit in Oxford until his retirement in 1976 and was also University Lecturer in Geriatric Medicine at the University of Oxford from 1960 to 1979.

By the time Cosin retired, the practice of geriatrics in this country had been transformed, thanks in no small part to his work. He was a founder member of the British Geriatrics Society. Since its inception, geriatrics has come a long way. It is seen in a positive light, unlike the virtually workhouse conditions of the past. Staff work as a multidisciplinary team, with detailed assessment and early intervention. Every medical school now has a department of geriatrics.

Lionel Cosin married Pamela Headlam in 1941. They had one son and one daughter. He died in London on 21 March 1994, aged eighty-three.

Doctor Sidney Truelove (1913–2002)

Ward 5F at the John Radcliffe Hospital is the gastroenterology and hepatology ward named after Doctor Truelove, who was a gastroenterologist in Oxford from 1947 to 1980. He was one of the founding fathers of academic gastroenterology throughout the world. There is also a recently endowed Truelove Chair of Gastroenterology in Oxford.

Sidney Charles Truelove was born in London on 24 February 1913 and grew up in a Cambridgeshire village, attending the local grammar school. He was the first of his family to go to university, winning an open scholarship to Trinity Hall, Cambridge. He did his clinical training at King's College, London, qualifying in 1938. He served in the Royal Army Medical Corps during the Second World War. Here he began the research which became an important part of his career. He did important work on the epidemiology of infectious hepatitis among British troops and also, whilst working in the War Office, was introduced to medical statistics. His work on hepatitis brought him to the attention of Professor Leslie Witts, the Nuffield Professor of Medicine at Oxford, and he invited Doctor Truelove to come and work with him in 1947. He was initially first assistant to Professor Witts and then became consultant and Reader in Medicine.

Doctor Truelove was a man of great intellect and a skilled clinical investigator, a stickler for scientific protocol. He contributed much to our knowledge and treatment of a wide range of diseases, including peptic ulcers, irritable bowel syndrome, coeliac disease, and inflammatory bowel disease. His greatest contribution, however, is his work on the treatment of ulcerative colitis, which has undoubtedly saved many lives.

In 1955, Truelove and Witts published the results of the first randomised placebo controlled trial of oral cortisone in active ulcerative colitis. It was certainly effective and mortality was greatly reduced. Then in 1958, Truelove showed that hydrocortisone locally, as a rectal drip, was effective in active ulcerative colitis. In 1978 he introduced intravenous treatment with glucocorticoids in severe attacks. This led to the 'Truelove Regimen' where intravenous steroids, intravenous fluids, and nutritional support were given and a decision made after a fixed period of days as to whether to continue medical treatment or proceed to colectomy. He always collaborated closely with surgeons to optimise treatment of the patient.

He also did important work on the role of sulphasalazine (salazopyrin) in ulcerative colitis. In 1973 he demonstrated that the drug greatly reduced the risk of relapse. This drug is a combination of an antibacterial sulphonamide and the aspirin-related drug 5-aminosalicylic acid (5ASA). In 1977 Truelove showed that it is the 5ASA that is the active ingredient, the sulphonamide transporting it to the colon. He applied the drug via an enema and showed that the 5ASA works topically. As the sulphonamide causes side-effects, drugs combining 5ASA with other chemicals have been developed that allow the salicylate to reach the colon without prior absorption. The use of high doses of 5ASA's has been a major advance in the treatment of ulcerative colitis and has allowed the use of steroids to be reduced dramatically.

Doctor Truelove was also a great and inspiring teacher, to medical students and to the postgraduate doctors from all over the world who came to work with him. If a student failed to come up to scratch on a ward round, he would be dispatched to the library and asked to do a presentation the next week. He loved Spain and a number of postgraduates came from Spain to work with him, and they recall his kindness and friendship. He would make sure they had somewhere suitable to stay and that their families were looked after too. He was patient and kindly if their English was halting. They recall his hospitality and warmth; they would be invited to dinner, or for walks around Oxford at sunset, and discuss all manner of subjects from the human to the divine. He liked even his young students and colleagues to call him by his Christian name. In return he visited Spain where he was a celebrated lecturer. Indeed, his textbook *Diseases of the Digestive System* was translated into Spanish. He visited and lectured in many other countries as well. As a result he has had a great influence on the specialty of gastroenterology throughout the world.

Doctor Truelove was a kindly and skilled clinician too. Despite his great abilities and success, he never lost the common touch and he could converse with all sorts of patient. He was a man of humanity and lacked all pomp.

He was undoubtedly an eccentric. He tended to arrive at the hospital at about 11.30 am and work through till 7.30 pm. When working with junior staff on a scientific paper or book, work would go on at his house till dawn, with cigarettes and whisky aplenty. He had an allotment where he grew vegetables which he would proudly show to his juniors. He was also keen on motoring and even persuaded drivers at the nearby lorry park to let him drive their trucks. *Diseases of the Digestive System* is a comprehensive and readable book. There are some delightful phrases: in his section on Crohn's disease he lists one of the presenting features as a 'loss of *joie-de-vivre*'.

Soon after his retirement, Doctor Truelove founded the International Organisation for Inflammatory Bowel Disease. He was the first physician in Britain to use a fibreoptic endoscope and became the first President of the British Society of Digestive Endoscopy. He was also President of the British Society of Gastroenterology.

Sidney Truelove died on 19 April 2002 at the age of eighty-nine. He was married to Joan, who outlived him and reached her hundredth birthday. They had two children, Anna and Richard.

Doctor Philip Bedford (*c.*1914–1962)

Bedford Ward on Level 4 at the John Radcliffe Hospital is an acute geratology ward named after Philip Bedford, general physician and geriatrician, who worked with Doctor Cosin in the world-class and pioneering care of the elderly in Oxford in the 1950s.

Philip Derek Bedford went to school in Leeds where he shone academically and gained a scholarship to read medicine at Leeds University. He qualified in 1939. He held a number of posts at Halifax General Hospital. He was a medical officer in the Royal Air Force during the Second World War, serving in India, Burma, and France. After the war he became a medical registrar at Leeds General Infirmary. He then worked as a registrar and senior registrar in Oxford, in the Cowley Road Hospital (pictured above). His abilities were soon recognised and he was made consultant in 1954, with care of the elderly among his responsibilities. He was also clinical lecturer and tutor in medicine in the University of Oxford.

He was able to apply his skills as an astute clinician to the care of the elderly. Thus, whilst recognising with Cosin (see earlier) the importance of social factors and the total care of elderly patients, Bedford made a special study of their medical problems. He was highly intelligent with an enquiring mind, always contributing to any medical discussion. His most important contribution was the observation that the elderly often suffered from multiple conditions resulting in multiple physiological disturbances. These were often inter-related and led to disabilities. He stressed the importance of a thorough examination of every system, and the patients' notes from the Cowley Road Hospital came with a long list of diagnoses. This was somewhat of a surprise for those who had been schooled in the philosophy of Occam's razor, trained to find a single explanation for a multitude of symptoms and signs.

Another important observation was that the results of medication could be worse than those of the underlying disease. Some patients were on a veritable concoction of drugs. He would use his skills as a physician to change the regimen, often withdrawing drugs, and this often led to improvement in the patient's condition.

Other research interests included the effects of anaesthetics in the elderly and the occurrence of post-operative disability.

He combined clinical prowess with great skill as a teacher to undergraduates and fellow doctors alike. In the elderly, students could learn about a wide variety of medical conditions, often a number in any one patient. This was intellectually challenging both from a medical and social point of view. His ward rounds were popular. Indeed, it was said that a good preparation for a membership examination was to attend Doctor Bedford's ward rounds. His enthusiastic approach enhanced the standing of the geriatric unit in the eyes of the university and the general physician.

Bedford was aware of the importance of an ethical approach and the need to know when to investigate and when to leave the elderly patient in peace. He was a compassionate man, a good friend to colleagues and to students, always willing to help and advise.

Sadly, Philip Bedford died suddenly in 1962 at the age of only forty-eight. As Professor Witts wrote in his obituary, it was a tragedy that a man so devoted to promoting longevity in others should die so young. He left a wife and son.

Professor George Adams (1916–2012)

Adams Ward on Level 4 at the John Radcliffe Hospital is an acute geratology ward named after George Adams, a pioneer in the field of academic geriatrics. In Belfast, he created the first purpose-built geriatric unit in the United Kingdom and was one of the first geriatricians to teach the subject to undergraduates. He was one of a group of doctors who revolutionised the care of the elderly from the mid-twentieth century. (See also articles on Doctor Lionel Cosin and Doctor Philip Bedford.)

George Fowler Adams was born in Yorkshire in 1916. He was educated in Northern Ireland and studied medicine at the Queen's University, Belfast, qualifying in 1938. He joined the Ulster division of the Royal Naval Volunteer Reserve, serving as a medical officer on board ships. He was called upon to perform an appendectomy on board one ship, and remained firm friends with the grateful patient.

Whilst working at the Royal Victoria Hospital in Belfast, he was inspired by his teacher Professor Thomson, who showed great care and compassion for elderly patients on the chronic sick wards of the Poor Law infirmaries. Thomson asked Adams to review these patients, with a view to deciding how their care would fit in to the impending National Health Service. Adams was so interested that he attended the inaugural meeting of the Medical Society for the Care of the Elderly in 1947, which later became the British Geriatrics Society.

Another doctor who inspired George was Marjory Warren (1897–1960), who is seen by many as the founder of modern geriatrics. Adams attended her ward rounds whilst working at the Hammersmith Hospital and on returning to Belfast saw what might be possible with the 'neglected human wreckage' in the overcrowded wards of the City Hospital.

Adams became a Consultant Physician in Geriatric Medicine at Belfast City Hospital in 1949, and honorary lecturer at Queen's University, Belfast. As Cosin had done in Orsett, Adams found himself responsible for a large number of elderly patients for whom there was really no hope. The conditions were poor with overcrowding, in what were really workhouse conditions. There were no resources for rehabilitation or treatment and it really amounted to passive custodial care.

Adams set about changing things. He campaigned for the introduction of a positive approach, where elderly patients were treated actively with the aim of restoring them to their full potential. There was an emphasis on diagnosing treatable conditions, and once these had been addressed, mobilising the patients. This allowed closure of beds.

Adams went on to found the first purpose-built geriatric unit in the United Kingdom, having persuaded the authorities to renovate wards at the Belfast City Hospital. He put together a team of nurses, social workers, and therapists who worked together for treatment and rehabilitation of the elderly sick.

His main research interest was the link between cardiovascular disease and disability in the elderly. One particular area in which the unit specialised was the restoration of function in hemiplegic patients. Visitors came from all around the world to visit the unit. He felt his most important paper was 'Mental Barriers to Recovery from Stroke'.

Not content with working locally, he campaigned to bring about changes in policy nationally. He carried out meticulous surveys, the results of which were used to influence policy for the development of medical services for the elderly. He lobbied the Royal College of Physicians to form a college committee for geriatrics.

His reputation spread abroad and he was visiting professor at the

University of Manitoba.

In 1971 Adams was made Professor of Geriatrics in Belfast. This was only the second chair in geriatrics in the United Kingdom. He served as President of the British Geriatrics Society from 1973 to 1975.

He and his wife retired to Oxfordshire where he was respected and loved for his grace, wisdom, and humour. He cared for his wife Mary who suffered from Alzheimer's disease. He would relate the story of a ward round where he hid his pen under a patient's pillow with a view to testing her memory. After examining her, he searched his pockets in vain for his pen, only for it to be retrieved by the patient from under the pillow with the words 'Is this what you're looking for?'

He lived a long and fruitful life, dying on 13 March 2012 from bronchopneumonia in his mid-nineties. He is survived by three children.

Professor John Ledingham,
Emeritus Professor of Clinical Medicine (1929–)

John Ledingham was a consultant physician in Oxford from 1966 until his retirement in 1995. From 1974 he was the May Reader in Medicine and from 1989 he was Professor of Clinical Medicine, University of Oxford. He is remembered fondly by many as Director of Clinical Studies. The bar at William Osler House, the medical students' club at the John Radcliffe Hospital, is named after him.

John Gerard Garvin Ledingham was born on 19 October 1929 in Ladbroke Square, London. He was educated at Rugby then did National Service in Hong Kong, serving as an officer in the Royal Artillery. It was here that he decided on a career in medicine. He came from a family of doctors and journalists, but despite dreams of editing the *Manchester Guardian*, and thoughts of being a teacher, he chose medicine. Not having done science at school, and having long spells of inactivity while stationed abroad, he purchased science textbooks and set about teaching himself in a tent in the Hong Kong New Territories.

On returning to Britain, he went up to New College in 1950. He then went to the Middlesex Hospital for his clinical training, qualifying in 1957. After junior appointments at the Middlesex, then as Senior Registrar at the Westminster, he spent a year as visiting fellow at Columbia University in New York, where he did research on renin, angiotensin, and hypertension. This was at a time when in order to be a consultant in a teaching hospital, one had to have some experience in research, most achieving this by going to America ('Been to America—BTA!').

In 1966 he was appointed consultant physician to the United Oxford Hospitals, in general medicine, endocrinology, diabetes, metabolic disease, and nephrology. It was at the time that Sir George Pickering (see earlier) was Regius Professor, and Professor Ledingham was one of five young consultants appointed, known as 'Pickering's boys'. Pickering was keen to heal the division between National Health Service consultants and those in the university departments, making all equally occupied and respected in teaching, research, and clinical work. Making use of the 'A+B' system then available, he enticed these new consultants to take two sessions in research instead of private practice. They were offered lectureships in the university and £500 per year and laboratory space. Professor Ledingham describes the sense of excitement in the Oxford Medical School at the time, largely due to Sir George's influence. Pickering was the major influence in changing the clinical school from one which few wished to join to the most sought after in the country. Although there were only a total of thirty students when Professor Ledingham arrived in 1966, there were 'take rounds' and 'grand rounds' and weekly 'Consilia' in which all were expected to present their research activities. It was an 'intellectual hothouse'.

Professor Ledingham has published over a hundred and fifty papers in the field of renal disease and hypertension, particularly on the connection between the kidney and hypertension and the role of renin, angiotensin, and aldosterone. He became May Reader in Medicine in 1974.

In 1989 he was made ad hominem Professor of Clinical Medicine. He partnered Sir David Weatherall on the Nuffield Department of Medicine for nineteen years, and this was a happy and felicitous union for students, junior staff, and patients alike. Both men were able scientists and clinicians, but also great teachers and above all, kind and humane doctors. He was one of the editors, together with Professor Weatherall and Professor Warrell, of the *Oxford Textbook of Medicine*. His ability to solve complex cases that had baffled other physicians was well known.

Professor Ledingham has played an important part in the development of the Oxford Clinical School, as Director of Clinical Studies from 1977 to 1981 and from 1991 to 1995. When he took up the post, there were some fifty clinical students a year. Continuing Professor Pickering's work, for five years he would visit Cambridge regularly, persuading students that they should come to Oxford. It got to the stage that so many people wanted to come, particularly from Cambridge, London, and St Andrew's, that 50 per cent had to be turned down. It was the place to which everyone wanted to go.

Professor Ledingham feels that the small size of the clinical school in the early days has been the key to its success over the years, compared with many other medical schools. This has allowed there to be a personal relationship between the staff and the students, which still exists. There is a healthy and refreshing attitude whereby a student is treated as an intellectual equal to the consultant, an important member of the team, able to have an opinion of his own.

Many of us will remember Professor Ledingham as a kind and approachable Director of Clinical Studies. He saw his role very much as a friend of the students, knowing every student personally and there to fight their battles. He was there in his office every morning at 8 o'clock, the door open for any student to drop in. He would see every new student between October and Christmas. As well as supporting and advising those in difficulty, he would guide students in their career. He had many contacts all over the country so that he had could help final year students find house jobs via the 'golden route'. He also encouraged students who were gifted and had interests outside clinical medicine, allowing them flexibility to spend time in, for example, politics, music, or cricket.

Professor Ledingham was Director of Clinical Studies at the time Green Templeton College came into being. In many ways this time of change was a difficult one for the clinical students, who feared the loss of William Osler House, their club and 'home' at the Radcliffe Infirmary.

During his time as Director of Clinical Studies, Professor Ledingham has, of course advised many women students on their career. His mother, wife, and daughter have all been doctors and he is a strong believer that women are good for medicine, more likely to treat the patient rather than the disease. It turns out that half the Nuffield Department of Medicine's house physicians are nearly always women. However, he is aware of the conflict many women doctors face, being channelled into medicine because they are bright, but some not being as ambitious as their male counterparts because of their wishes to have a family.

As a distinguished teacher and clinician, Professor Ledingham has some interesting views on what makes a good doctor. He feels passionately that a very broad and extensive experience is essential. When he became a consultant, he had seen an enormously wide spectrum of diseases across all the major specialties. He recalls how, in his first year as a doctor, he 'lived' in the hospital, only spending a handful of hours outside it during the whole year. There was a barber and a bank in the hospital, and the junior doctors rarely left it. He spent every hour of the day with his patients and would be called any time of day or night if one of his own patients became ill. It gave one a sense of personal responsibility to the patient. Seeing patients throughout the course of their illness taught one in the best way how to relate and talk to them—much better than formal teaching of 'communication skills'. He recalls one of his patients, a young woman who remained on the ward for months, dying of breast cancer. He spent half an hour, twice a day with her, so learning much about the care of the dying. He feels that with the passing of this way of life and of the continuity of care, we have lost something.

Another aspect which he believes we have lost today is the importance of the role model. One would work longer for one particular consultant in those days and if he was a man of reputation and charisma, the junior doctor could learn so much by osmosis. He would learn clinical skills, but also how to handle patients, which goes so far beyond the science of medicine. Conversely, one could learn how not to treat patients from a consultant who did not have good skills. He recalls the house staff having to go round the ward after one consultant's rounds, reassuring tearful patients.

His first house job was for the distinguished neurologist Michael

Kremer, from whom he learned a great deal. Another neurologist who inspired him was Valentine Logue, the son of the speech therapist who treated King George VI (immortalised in the film 'The King's Speech'). Indeed, Professor Ledingham might well have specialised in neurology had he not moved into renal medicine.

Since his retirement, Professor Ledingham has continued to help the clinical students. When clinical teaching commenced at the Radcliffe Infirmary at the outset of the Second World War, the eighteenth-century Observer's House adjacent to the Radcliffe Infirmary became the common room and bar for the students. Lord Nuffield, who had purchased the land for the hospital, named it Osler House because of his friendship with Sir William Osler. When the John Radcliffe Hospital opened in 1979, Osler House was housed in the former Administrator's House on the hospital site. Over the years, it became in need of refurbishment, and in 2009 Professor Ledingham was instrumental in raising considerable funds, largely from an alumnus who wanted to help the medical school, for the refurbishment and extension of Osler House. In recognition of this, the bar is named after him. Osler House now provides wonderful facilities for the clinical students. As well as the bar and a coffee shop, there is a lecture and musical performance room, and an IT suite and offices for student societies. The gardens have been landscaped and the restoration has been sympathetically done to reflect the house's Art Deco style. It is an important 'home' and retreat for the clinical students.

Professor Ledingham also played an important part in the founding of the Oxford Medical Alumni and was its first president. He guided its emergence from the old Oxford Graduates Medical Club, a dining club founded in 1884. The aim of this organisation, of which every Oxford medical graduate is a member, is to establish a fruitful, mutually beneficial relationship between the alumni and the medical school. There are events in the United Kingdom, Europe, and North America ranging from purely social ones and reunions to lectures and medical meetings. There are annual Weatherall and Osler Lectures in Oxford. Graduates are kept abreast of the Oxford medical scene and it is a forum for meeting other medical alumni.

In October 2011 Professor Ledingham received the Distinguished Friend of Oxford Award, given by the Vice-Chancellor for services of a voluntary capacity to the university. This was in recognition of his long service to the hospitals as a clinician and teacher, as well as his work since retirement for Osler House and the Oxford Medical Alumni. Over the years he has sat on many committees and been an examiner at a number of medical schools. He is a former President of the British Hypertension Society. He was a trustee of the Nuffield Trust for twenty-five years.

Professor Ledingham is an enthusiastic sportsman. He was a hockey 'blue' and also captained Scotland at hockey in 1957. He plays golf well and enthusiastically and also enjoys fly fishing. He enjoys listening to music, especially opera.

To sum up, I think it is worth quoting some words Professor Ledingham's father said to him. He was a graduate of Aberdeen University and a GP in London. He said, 'You can get pleasure for making a fine scientific discovery, or from making a correct diagnosis in a difficult case, when all others are puzzled—but in the end you will find that these are vanity compared with the sense of achievement you will get when you have spent time with a patient ill with an unmanageable or terminal disease for which there is no useful treatment, and left them happier and better from your time talking to them.' This very much sums up Professor Ledingham's approach. Like his father, he believes that a doctor should remember he should be a servant, not a master, to his patients. When his mother retired from the Royal Free Hospital in 1965, engraved on the silver salver presented to her were the words 'with gratitude for the inspiration of a great teacher, not only of medicine, but also of the ways of human beings'. These words could equally be applied to her son.

Professor Sir David Weatherall,
Regius Professor of Medicine Emeritus (1933–)

Sir David Weatherall was Nuffield Professor of Clinical Medicine at Oxford from 1974 to 1992 then Regius Professor of Medicine until his retirement in 2000. He founded what was later to become the Weatherall Institute of Molecular Medicine at the John Radcliffe Hospital in 1989. There is also an annual Weatherall Lecture, part of the Oxford Medical Alumni programme. One of his major achievements has been encouraging the combination of clinical medicine and scientific research. He is well known for his work on the haemoglobinopathies and in particular the thalassaemias, where he has led the way in encouraging links between Oxford and developing countries.

David John Weatherall was born in 1933 and educated at Calday Grange Grammar School in the Wirral. He read medicine at Liverpool, qualifying in 1956. After house jobs and time as a senior house officer, he did military service where he was posted to Singapore for two years. Although he had no experience of paediatrics, he was put in charge of a large children's ward in a military hospital. Here he came across a child with thalassaemia called Jaspir Thapa, the daughter of a Nepalese Gurkha who was serving in Malaya. She is perhaps his most memorable patient and the one who has had most influence on his career. When Jaspir's father finished his spell in the British Army, the family returned to Nepal, but the lack of facilities meant that she could not have survived for long. Lady Mountbatten, who was the head of the Red Cross, took a great interest in the child and Lord Mountbatten had a drawing made of Jaspir with Lady Mountbatten. It was the plight of this girl that made Sir David embark on his work on the genetics of blood disorders.

So, on finishing National Service, Sir David spent four years at Johns Hopkins University in Baltimore in the United States, which was in the forefront of research into medical genetics. Whilst there he worked in genetics, haematology, biophysics, and protein chemistry as well as maintaining an interest in general medicine. He returned to Liverpool, eventually becoming Professor of Haematology there.

He was appointed Nuffield Professor of Clinical Medicine in Oxford in 1974. On arriving in Oxford he found the clinical school in good shape, but saw the need for more research. The scientists in Parks Road had little contact with the clinicians, and the two viewed each other with mutual suspicion. He set about remedying this, and developed research projects in Oxford including research into the genetics of the thalassaemias. These are a complex group of disorders resulting from gene mutations that lead to reduced or absent production of globin chains, the protein components of haemoglobin. Ability of the cells to carry oxygen is impaired, leading to anaemia, and this is exacerbated by haemolysis of the affected cells.

There are two main types, alpha thalassaemias which occur largely in South-East Asia, and beta thalassaemias occurring in Mediterranean countries as well as Africa and Asia. The major forms occur when the patient is homozygous, both copies of the gene being affected. The clinical picture varies greatly. In the severest cases, the foetus dies. Children may become sick from birth, failing to thrive; many require frequent blood transfusion. The high level of these gene abnormalities in affected areas may be because heterozygous carriers have some resistance to *P. falciparum* malaria.

Nowadays we are accustomed to global health enterprises and research partnerships, but as long ago as the 1970s, Sir David adopted this approach with thalassaemia.

It has continued to the present day as illustrated by the case of Kurenegala, a place in Sri Lanka with the highest incidence of thalassaemia. After he had given a lecture at the Sri Lankan College of Physicians in the mid-nineties, Sir David was approached by a paediatrician from Kurenegala who asked for his help and advice. This doctor was regularly transfusing the children. Professor Weatherall arranged for blood samples from children all over the island to be sent back to Oxford for analysis. It turned out that a third of the children had a mild form of the disease and did not require transfusion (which is itself harmful because of the accumulation of iron in the tissues). These patients adapt to their anaemia and are able to work on the land until their forties or fifties.

Professor Weatherall saw the lack of facilities at the District General Hospital in Kurenegala, where children were left to die, and mothers had to sleep on the floor while their child was being transfused. He arranged for a local young man to do a DPhil at Oxford and then work in the field on his return to Sri Lanka. Furthermore, he raised funds for the building of a thalassaemia screening and treatment centre attached to the paediatric ward at the hospital. He found a retired architect who would design the unit for free. The Sri Lankan Government and the Wellcome Trust paid for some of the building. On retiring as a trustee of the Wellcome Trust in 2000, Sir David asked if, instead of the customary lavish dinner, the money could be given to the centre, and it was put towards equipping the unit.

Work continues in a number of countries and Sir David continues to play an active part. DNA diagnostic centres have been set up in many areas and national programmes of screening are being developed. Genetic testing and counselling of future parents is very important, but there are very few counsellors, and cultural factors such as the male refusing to accept that he could be at fault makes work difficult.

As far as treatment is concerned, there has been some success with bone marrow transplantation, but it has been slow getting off the ground and there is no centre yet in Sri Lanka. There is a modest transplant programme in Thailand and good progress has been made in India. It is best done early in life. Gene therapy will be important in the future, but again progress is slow and there are the difficulties of developing such complex and expensive treatments in the developing world. The advances in treatment leading to life expectancy being improved considerably brings its own problems, as there are no doctors to look after the children once they reach fourteen and leave the fold of the paediatricians.

Another important field is that of prenatal diagnosis, which is cost-effective and a way of ensuring a normal child, but is not acceptable to some religious groups. It has not always been easy, with national and local politics to contend with and the need for locals to accept experts from another country telling them what to do.

When Sir David came to Oxford he saw that the future of medical research would be at the molecular and cellular level and over the years felt that there was a need for somewhere where clinicians could be trained in these techniques. At the same time DPhil students with a background of basic science could work in the same environment. Eventually, the Medical Research Council offered funding, and help was also obtained from the Wolfson Foundation and the University of Oxford as well as Cancer Research UK and the Wellcome Trust. So in 1989 the Institute of Molecular Medicine was opened at the John Radcliffe Hospital. It encourages research in molecular and cell biology and its application to human disease. Some four hundred scientists work there, on a wide range of topics. These include the genetics of blood disorders as described above as well as the regulation of the elements of the blood in relation to malignant diseases of the blood. Other projects include the genetic basis of facial deformities, AIDS and HIV, various aspects of research into cancer, and parasitology.

Upon Sir David's retirement in 2000 the Institute was named after him. It has proved a very effective way of bringing together clinicians and research scientists. It has also fostered important beneficial partnerships with developing countries, of which Sir David is very proud. Thus there are major overseas programmes in global health and tropical medicine in many countries in Africa and Asia.

Over the years, Sir David has seen changes in the medical school too. He oversaw the beginning of the graduate entry medical course which, though brought in with some degree of trepidation, has proved successful. Mention should also be made of the *Oxford Textbook of Medicine*, first published in 1983, which Sir David edited with Professor John Ledingham and Professor David Warrell. It was felt that there was a need for a new general textbook of medicine with global coverage rather than the standard Western book. It has been a success. One problem is the high cost for those in developing countries, but it is interesting that Oxford students doing their elective abroad do find it in hospital libraries in far-flung countries.

Sir David has held a number of advisory posts, some of them in the field of medical ethics. He was a founder member of the Nuffield Council on Bioethics. In 2002 he wrote a major report for the World Health Organisation on the application of genomics for global health.

In his book, *Science and the Quiet Art: Medical Research and Patient Care* (Oxford, 1995), he traces the development of scientific medicine over the past one hundred and fifty years up to the modern molecular and cell biology of today. Looking at the range of disease in both the western and developing worlds, he discusses the complexities of the interactions of the environment and the genes and how we still have so much to learn. The advances that have demonstrated abnormal genes partially or wholly responsible for a disorder have created exciting possibilities for treatment. But they have also created whole new ethical dilemmas that make the 'art' of medicine, which includes compassion and humanity, more important than ever.

Whilst working in Baltimore, Sir David met his wife Stella who comes from Columbia in South America. She was working in the biochemistry department at Johns Hopkins. She is a talented artist. They have a son, Mark, who is a consultant neurologist in London. Outside medicine, Sir David's main hobby has always been music, mainly as a listener but he also plays the piano and spinette.

Sir David has been Chancellor of Keele University and helped set up a medical school there. He was knighted in 1987 and is a Fellow of the Royal Society, as well as an overseas member of the National Academy of Sciences of America. In 2010, Sir David was awarded a Lasker Award. This important American prize is awarded for outstanding medical research and was awarded to Sir David for 'fifty years of international statesmanship in biomedical science'.

Sir David has undoubtedly made an enormous contribution to the field of molecular medicine and to haematology in particular. But equally important is the wide range of his approach to medicine; he is interested in every aspect from molecular genetics to the clinical care, from public health issues to ethics. He has contributed much to medical education too. Both on meeting him, and on reading his books, one is struck by his humanity and kindness.

Professor Sir Peter Morris,
Nuffield Professor of Surgery Emeritus (1934–)

Ward 6C at the John Radcliffe Hospital is a vascular surgical ward named after Sir Peter Morris, Nuffield Professor of Surgery at Oxford from 1974 until 2001. He is a pioneer in the field of immunology and transplant surgery and has done important work on the role of Human Leucocyte Antigen (HLA) in transplantation and disease. His major contributions in Oxford include founding the Oxford Transplant Centre and establishing a major vascular unit. He is also cofounder of the Wellcome Trust Centre for Human Genetics.

Peter John Morris was born in a country town called Horsham, some two hundred miles from Melbourne, Australia, on 7 April 1934. He was educated at Xavier College before moving on to the University of Melbourne to read medicine. His father was a civil engineer and Australian Rules Football champion but sadly died when Peter was only fourteen years old. Peter inherited his father's love of sport and played both cricket and baseball for the university.

Sir Peter qualified in 1957 and began his surgical training at St Vincent's Hospital, Melbourne. It was customary to complete one's training overseas, as there was no comprehensive training programme in surgery in Australia at that time. He therefore came to Britain in 1961 and worked at Guy's, the Hammersmith, and Southampton.

He then moved to America and worked as senior resident in surgery at the Massachusetts General Hospital (MGH) for a year before spending two years as research fellow at Harvard with Jack Burke, studying various aspects of infection in the surgical wound and in the burn patient. There was an active renal transplant programme at the MGH and this is where he became interested in the field of histocompatibility testing and transplant immunology. Following training by Paul Terasaki at UCLA, he was then asked by David Hume to set up a tissue typing laboratory at the Medical College of Virginia, by then the largest transplant unit in the world. Here was a stroke of fortune: there was a freezer full of serum taken from patients before and after renal transplant. Sir Peter was the first to show that human cytotoxic antibodies were present in transplant recipients in whom rejection occurred. They were donor specific. This led him to believe they might have a key role in the mechanism of rejection, not accepted wisdom at that time.

He returned to Melbourne in late 1967 as third assistant in the University of Melbourne Department of Surgery under Professor Maurice Ewing, rising to be Reader in Surgery by 1972. There was already a good renal transplant unit there and he was able to establish another tissue typing unit and continue his research and clinical work in transplantation as well as undertake a general surgical commitment. His laboratories there developed renal transplantation in the rat, a microsurgical tour de force at the time. This model allowed him and his group to produce tolerance to a foreign kidney using a variety of techniques to manipulate the host immune response.

In 1974 he was invited to Oxford as Nuffield Professor of Surgery and Chairman of the Department of Surgery. Here he combined his research into the immunology of transplantation with the work of a busy vascular and general surgeon. He established a vascular unit at the Radcliffe Infirmary, where he had his laboratories, and the transplant unit at the Churchill Hospital.

Sir Peter brought research workers and clinicians from all over Australia to work with him, and the Nuffield department became known as 'Kangaroo Valley'. It was an exciting time and the department thrived. When the Nuffield department moved to the new John

Radcliffe Hospital in 1979, there were excellent facilities for research and as previously his laboratories were on the same level as his clinical wards. Sir Peter was able to gain funding soon after he arrived from the Medical Research Council for a long-term programme grant in the field of transplant immunology. Work included studies on human leucocyte antigens (HLA) and immunological tolerance as well as studies on HLA in suspected autoimmune diseases such as type 1 diabetes. He has overseen the introduction of new methods, such as the transition from serological HLA typing to molecular techniques for tissue typing.

Prior to Sir Peter's arrival, there was no renal transplant unit in Oxford. The story of kidney transplantation goes back as far as 1936 when a series of deceased donor kidney transplants was performed in Russia. Then in the late 1940s similar attempts were made in America and in Paris, but again with no success. The breakthrough came in December 1954 when a patient with renal failure at the Peter Bent Brigham Hospital in Boston was found to have an identical twin. A kidney was transplanted from his twin brother and the operation was successful. The patient married his nurse and had two children, but sadly died eight years later due to recurrence of the original disease in the transplanted kidney. This was the first successful renal transplant from a living donor. It was an important event and caused great excitement as it showed that, if matched, a transplanted kidney would not be rejected and could function normally.

Oxford had the biggest dialysis unit in Europe at that time run by the big ex-New Zealand All Black, Des Oliver. There were some two hundred patients on dialysis, and some patients were referred to Birmingham or Cambridge for transplantation but with poor results. The first renal transplant in Oxford was carried out by Sir Peter at the Churchill Hospital on 29 January 1975 in the evening, and the second after midnight. The operations and those following were very successful so that, after initial reluctance, some hundred patients went onto the waiting list.

Initially the transplant team used beds on the urology wards at the Churchill, but then a specialised unit, funded by Dame Rosemary Rue, was built in 1978 at the end of the new renal unit and was formally opened by Sir Peter Medawar. This was soon too small so Sir Peter Morris raised money for a new and larger unit. This included laboratories for tissue typing, immunological monitoring, and pancreatic islet transplantation, the main laboratories remaining in the Nuffield Department of Surgery at the John Radcliffe. The new facility was opened in 1992 as the Oxford Transplant Centre. In 1975, fifty transplants were carried out but this number soon increased and now many more are done with the unit having performed over three thousand renal transplants and several hundred pancreatic transplants, both as whole organ transplants and islet transplants.

Sir Peter retired from the Nuffield Chair in 2001 and was then elected as President of the Royal College of Surgeons of England for three years. He was the first surgeon from Oxford to ever serve as president. In 2005 he founded an organisation called the Centre for Evidence in Transplantation (CET), which is based at the Royal College of Surgeons and the London School of Hygiene and Tropical Medicine as well as in Oxford. With a team of research associates and research fellows, the aim is to provide a source of high quality evidence-based information which is easily available to clinicians. The CET has established an electronic library of all randomised controlled trials in organ transplantation since the first in 1971. It requires no sophisticated search skill to use and the information is updated every two weeks. The CET also carries out systemic reviews of controversial topics in transplantation.

Sir Peter has won many prizes and accolades and held many important positions such as the President of the International Surgical Society, the European Surgical Association, and the International Transplant Society. He has been awarded numerous Honorary Fellowships and degrees and has been a visiting professor in some fifty institutions. In 1997 he was awarded the Lister Medal, the most prestigious prize in surgery and in 2006 he was awarded the Medawar Prize for his work on HLA in clinical transplantation. He was elected as a Fellow of the Royal Society in 1994 and was knighted in 1996. In 2004 he was made a Companion of the Order of Australia (AC) for his contributions to medical science. He has written many scientific papers and is editor of *Kidney Transplantation: Principles and Practice* which has had seven editions since the first in 1978, and of the first two editions of the *Oxford Textbook of Surgery*.

Sir Peter is married to a doctor, Jocelyn, whom he met at medical school in Melbourne. She ran the Lung Function Laboratory for the Chest Unit in Oxford (a post she owed in the first instance to Dame Rosemary Rue, see section on Old Road Campus). They have five children, two of whom are doctors. He still plays a little golf. Indeed, when he was a castaway on Desert Island Discs on Radio 4, his luxury was a set of golf clubs and balls.

One of the greatest influences on Sir Peter's surgical career was the surgeon Claude Welch under whom he worked at the Massachusetts General Hospital. Welch was always polite and courteous in theatre, saying please and thank you to those working with him. Sir Peter has followed in his footsteps, something those of us who were medical students in Oxford remember. It made a big impression on us and I hope it will be passed on to future generations of surgeons.

Professor Derek Jewell,
Emeritus Professor of Gastroenterology (1941–)

The Day Case Unit on Level 5 at the John Radcliffe Hospital is named after Derek Jewell, Emeritus Professor of Gastroenterology at the University of Oxford. The laboratory on Level 5 in the gastroenterology unit is also named after him. He has played a major role in upholding gastroenterology as an academic discipline and has done important work on the pathogenesis of inflammatory bowel disease and coeliac disease.

Derek Parry Jewell was born on 14 June 1941 in St Austell. His parents came from Bristol, but his father was stationed in Cornwall during the war and his mother lived there because of the heavy bombing in Bristol. Towards the end of the war the family returned to Bristol and Professor Jewell won a place at Bristol Grammar School. He won an Open Exhibition to Pembroke College, Oxford to read medicine. Even as an undergraduate he was interested in gastroenterology. His tutor was a biochemist with an interest in iron and vitamin B12 absorption. Then as a clinical student on the Nuffield Department of Medicine he was taught by Professor Leslie Witts, who was a clinical haematologist, and by his senior colleagues, Sheila Callender and Sidney Truelove (see earlier). The major interests in the department included studying the absorption of iron and B12 as well as treating gastrointestinal disease. This strongly influenced his subsequent career.

He qualified in 1966 and did his house jobs in Oxford before moving on to the Hammersmith Hospital which he found a stimulating experience. He then returned to Oxford to work for Doctor Sidney Truelove, who was an eminent gastroenterologist, and who encouraged Professor Jewell to do a DPhil with him. The subject was the immunology of inflammatory bowel disease. In 1973 Professor Jewell went to America for a year as assistant professor at Stanford University School of Medicine. On his return he became senior lecturer in medicine at the Royal Free Hospital in London, working for Dame Sheila Sherlock. In 1980 he took over from Sidney Truelove as consultant gastroenterologist in Oxford, and then became professor when a new chair was created.

A fascinating anecdote is worth telling. The first description in the literature of ulcerative colitis was always understood to be that of Wilks and Moxon in 1878 in the Pathological Treatises of Guy's Hospital. While doing his DPhil, Professor Jewell went to the Bodleian Library to read the original. It is a good description of a relapsing and remitting disease which the authors distinguished from bacterial dysentery, which was very common in Victorian London. Professor Jewell then noticed on the title page that this was the 2nd edition, and wondered why nobody ever mentioned the 1st edition. So he ordered it at the Bodleian and when he came to read it, he found that all the pages were uncut: nobody had ever read it! The librarian handed Professor Jewell a paper knife and he cut the pages himself! He found a chapter by Wilks which was a good description of ulcerative colitis as early as 1859. It is a series of case reports with a discussion of how they differ from other causes of bloody diarrhoea.

In the *Medical Gazette* of London in the same year Wilks wrote a case report about the 'colon of the unfortunate Miss Banks', whom he suspected had this new disease. There was, however, a suspicion that she might be the victim of mercury poisoning and indeed there was evidence of this. The suspect was her doctor who appeared in court but was acquitted. A few years later, he appeared in court again on a charge of poisoning and this time he was found guilty and hanged.

Our understanding of the pathology of ulcerative colitis has changed enormously in recent years. In 1909 there was a symposium at the Royal Society of Medicine at which a series of three hundred cases from the London teaching hospitals were studied. It was a lively meeting with plenty of difference of opinion. One group favoured an infectious aetiology, another diet, in particular a result of canning food or preservatives, and a third group favoured a psychosomatic cause. In the first edition of Truelove and Reynell's textbook *Diseases of the Digestive System* (1963), the aetiology is still unknown and the suggested causes are pretty much the same as in 1909, with the addition of the suggestion of an autoimmune cause. However, great strides have been made since then, in particular the knowledge of a genetic susceptibility to the disease. This is where Professor Jewell's work comes in, with his studies of the genetics and immunology of inflammatory bowel disease.

It was known that ulcerative colitis and Crohn's disease were sometimes found in more than one member of a family, suggesting the cause was not entirely environmental. There must be a genetic susceptibility. There was a high concordance in monozygotic twins. Professor Jewell set about finding the gene or genes responsible. In the early 1990s, genome-wide linkage studies were developed where markers are taken across the genome in large numbers of patients and control populations. By studying affected families and by applying basic Mendelian genetics it is possible to show that a disease is associated with the genetic marker. This allows one to narrow down the segment of the gene that is responsible for the disease. Professor Jewell's team in Oxford was one of the first to assemble a cohort of affected siblings and parents. More recently the technique of genome-wide scans has allowed further elucidation of the genetics and now almost two hundred genetic mutations have been found to be associated with ulcerative colitis and Crohn's disease. It is interesting that about forty are common to both diseases.

Work is under way into finding how the genetic mutations lead to disease. Many of the genetic polymorphisms associated with either ulcerative colitis or Crohn's disease can be grouped into a number of functional pathways that include epithelial barrier function, antigen recognition, immune regulation and intra-cellular signalling. Almost certainly, the normal host defence against intestinal bacteria can be affected by many of these genetic mutations and may therefore underly the chronic inflammatory nature of these diseases. At present, there is excitement about results of a study showing that multiple courses of antibiotics in the first two years of life are associated with an increased incidence of inflammatory bowel disease later in life.

Professor Jewell's other main interest is coeliac disease where he led research into the immune response to gluten. He has studied the part of the gliadin molecule, the glycoprotein component of gluten which acts as an antigen and produces a T cell immune response in coeliac patients. Susceptibility to coeliac disease is genetically controlled and all patients have either HLA-DR3 or HLA-DQ2 histocompatibility antigens, but of course this alone does not cause the disease. It is a complex condition but work is going on whereby the aminoacid sequences that stimulate the immune response to gluten are being determined. This may allow peptides to be given to coeliac patients which will block the T cell immune response and so obviate the need for a gluten-free diet.

Professor Jewell is aware of the privilege of working in Oxford where he has been able to collaborate with experts in related fields, such as the Weatherall Institute of Molecular Medicine and the Wellcome Centre for Human Genetics.

Two physicians in particular inspired Professor Jewell during his student days at Oxford and beyond. One was Professor Witts, the Nuffield Professor of Medicine. The other was Doctor Sidney Truelove, who was one of the fathers of academic gastroenterology worldwide.

Professor Jewell has always been keen that academic gastroenterology should have a future, and since his appointment as consultant in Oxford in 1980 has fought to make the post an academic one. In an exciting recent development, he persuaded the university to create a full-time endowed chair, the Truelove Chair of Gastroenterology. A new department has been created on Level 5 at the John Radcliffe Hospital with state-of-the-art laboratories and room for some thirty research scientists. There are two senior lecturers and these are full-time research posts but do two clinical sessions a week. In recognition of the role Professor Jewell played in setting up the unit, the laboratory is named after him. The Jewell Day Case Unit, also on Level 5 at the John Radcliffe Hospital, is used for procedures that do not require overnight admission.

Professor Jewell was president of the British Society of Gastroenterology from 2001 to 2002. He has been a member of the editorial board of a number of journals and has published several books. These include *Clinical Gastrointestinal Immunology* (1979) and *Challenges in Inflammatory Bowel Disease* (2000, 2nd edition 2006). He has been president of the Oxford Medical Alumni and editor of *Oxford Medicine*.

Professor Jewell is married to Barbara, a biology school teacher. They have a son who is a lecturer in biostatistics in New Zealand and a daughter who is a zoologist, now working for the RSPB. His main hobbies are gardening, reading, and music. He is an enthusiastic player of the violin and organ.

Overall, Professor Jewell feels proud that on following on from Sidney Truelove, he has been able to build on what he began and uphold the cause of academic gastroenterology. He himself has made a major contribution to the field.

Photo: Sir Michael (centre) and Lady Betty Kadoorie together with Professor Keith
Willett at the opening of the extension of the Kadoorie Centre on 12 July, 2013

Sir Michael Kadoorie (1941–)

The Kadoorie Centre on Level 3 of the Academic Centre at the John Radcliffe Hospital is named after Michael Kadoorie, businessman and philanthropist from Hong Kong. It is a centre for education and research in the field of critical illness and severe trauma, aimed at developing knowledge to improve the lot of such patients.

Michael David Kadoorie was born in Hong Kong in 1941. He was educated in Hong Kong and Switzerland. His grandfather came originally from Baghdad and made his fortune in Shanghai and Hong Kong in utilities, finance, and property. Michael is now the Chairman of the extensive family business, CLP Holdings Limited. Among many interests worldwide, the company provides 75 per cent of the electricity of Hong Kong. He has founded the CLP Research Institute which looks into renewable energy provision.

Sir Michael is interested in fast cars and owns a number of rare automobiles. It was this hobby that led to his connection with the John Radcliffe Hospital in 1998. He had an accident in a vintage Ferrari in the area, and this resulted in serious injuries which led to him spending two months as a patient at the John Radcliffe recovering. As a mark of his gratitude, he provided funding for the Kadoorie Centre for Critical Care Research and Education. It opened in 2003 in a purpose-built unit.

There are extensive education facilities including a lecture theatre and teleconference suite. The unit houses the Radcliffe Trust's resuscitation department. The simulation suite teaches resuscitation and life support on an advanced computer-controlled 'SimMan' training mannequin. There is a 'Scenario Theatre' which can be configured as a resuscitation bay, intensive care bed space, ambulance, acute hospital bed space, or out of hospital area. This allows a whole range of clinical situations to be simulated and training given.

Hands-on training is available to all hospital staff for whom it is relevant (including both those using complex medical equipment and the engineers who repair and maintain it). It is also open to those from outside for whom life support is an important skill and to medical staff from other regions.

As far as research is concerned, there are many projects underway, the emphasis being on large multicentre randomised controlled trials. In the field of trauma these include study of different types of mechanical support for fractures. In the field of serious illness, there are studies aimed at identifying early deterioration in patients in intensive care units and studying their long-term outcome.

The Kadoorie Centre needed to expand and in 2012 Michael Kadoorie was again generous in providing financial support. Michael lives in Hong Kong and is married with three children. Among many awards, he received a knighthood in 2005.

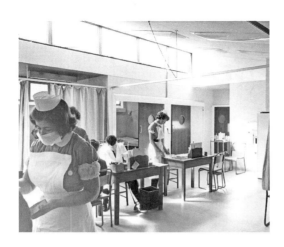

Sister Howells

Ward 5E at the John Radcliffe Hospital is a haematology ward and it seems probable that it is named after Sister Howells, who was the nursing sister on Lower Ward at the Radcliffe Infirmary. As was the custom in those days, she was always known as 'Sister Lower'. Lower Ward at the Radcliffe Infirmary had looked after haematology patients, so it is fitting that when the medical firms were reorganised at the John Radcliffe Hospital in 1990, the dedicated haematology ward should be named after Sister Howells.

She had previously been Sister on Collier Ward at the Radcliffe Infirmary. We know she was 'Sister Collier' in the early 1950s as she and her nursing staff are thanked for their help by Professor Leslie Witts in articles in the *British Medical Journal* on pernicious anaemia and folic acid at that time. One first-year nurse who arrived on the ward in 1956 recalls what a brilliant and efficient nurse Sister Collier was, but very strict and severe. Everyone was in awe of her, doctors included. Indeed, one recounts how he only stayed on for tea on the ward on her days off.

It seems she was a somewhat round Welsh lady, who 'stomped' about running a well-ordered ward and earning the respect of those with whom she came into contact.

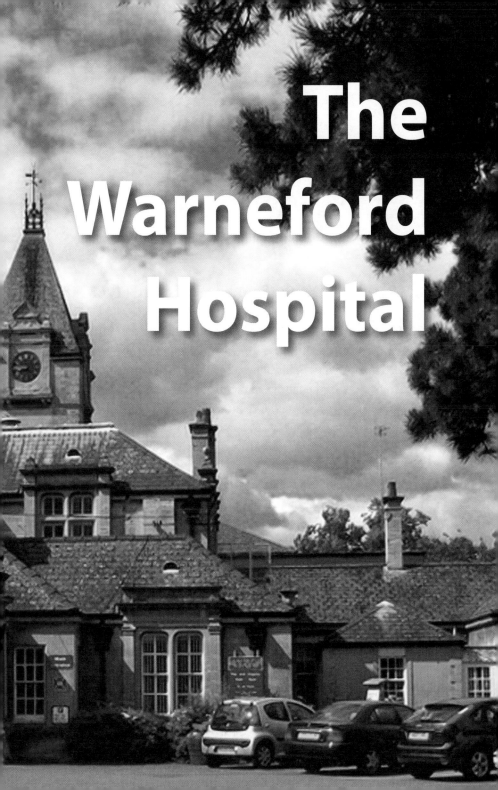

The
Warneford
Hospital

The Reverend Doctor Samuel Warneford (1763–1855)

The Warneford Hospital in Oxford is named after the philanthropist Samuel Warneford, who was a somewhat eccentric country parson who amassed great wealth in his lifetime. He inherited large sums of money from both sides of the family, often through absence of a male heir. He gave of it generously to medical, educational, and religious causes and over his lifetime he gave away some £200,000. His support for the Oxford Lunatic Asylum led to its being named after him in 1843.

Samuel Wilson Warneford was born in Sussex on 5 February 1763. His father Francis came of an old county family who had lived in the manor of Sevenhampton near Highworth in Wiltshire since at least the fourteenth century. The house, named Warneford Place, was built in 1566. Francis inherited the family estates in Wiltshire and Ireland in 1755. Further wealth came Francis's way when, at the age of twenty-five, he married one Catherine Calverley. She was the eldest daughter of a wealthy drug merchant who owned substantial freehold property in London and the home counties. Catherine was said to be no great beauty but to have a good business head (which she certainly passed on to her son Samuel).

Samuel was their second son, and there were two daughters. Samuel was a delicate child, so it is somewhat of a surprise that he lived to ninety-two. It is likely that the children were tutored at home in Warneford Place. We know that Samuel and his elder brother went up to Oxford in December 1779, entering University College as commoners. Samuel was very shy and found it hard to make friends with his hunting, drinking fellow-students. He read Law and took his MA in 1786. He was ordained deacon later that year and appointed curate of Yelford near Witney at a salary of £30 per annum. The master and fellows of University College had testified that he had resided for nineteen weeks over three years and lived a 'pious, sober and regular life'. It seems he was a reserved man, with no sense of humour.

In 1787 Samuel was ordained priest and appointed curate of Brize Norton in Oxfordshire. Then fortune came his way. In November 1791 his mother and aunt conveyed in trust to Samuel and his sister Philadelphia the landed property that they had inherited from their father.

The Warneford family became friendly with the Loveden family of Buscot Park, some few miles from Warneford Place. In June 1792, one Edward Loveden Loveden wrote an angry letter to Samuel because it appears he had proposed to his daughter Margaret Loveden, then 'scarcely of an age to leave the nursery', without asking his permission. Samuel was banned from the house and Margaret made a ward of court. When Margaret reached her twenty-first birthday in 1796, a marriage settlement was drawn up (with great reluctance on the part of her father) and on 27 September 1796 Samuel and Margaret married in Colney Hatch in Middlesex. No members of either family were there.

Within five years, Margaret had become seriously ill, but there was still no contact with her family. Her father still believed Samuel had designs on her money and tried to bring about a review of the marriage settlement. She had inherited a large sum of money from her maternal grandfather by this time. She and Samuel were not blessed with children.

After a number of appointments, in 1810 Samuel bought for the sum of £12,285 the advowson of Bourton-on-the-Hill, near Moreton-in-Marsh in Gloucestershire. It was worth £600 per annum. The household consisted of Samuel and his wife Margaret, his mother Catherine, who was now aged eighty-four, and his sister Philadelphia. Through the deaths of two aunts, and then in 1810 the death of their mother

Catherine, Samuel and his sister Philadelphia became very rich indeed. A few days after his mother's death, Samuel was instituted Rector of Saint Lawrence, Bourton-on-the-Hill, to which was attached the Chapelry of Moreton-in-Marsh. The same year he became a Doctor of Civil Law. Samuel felt the rectory at Bourton-on-the-Hill to be unsuitable, so built a new one.

We now begin to hear of Samuel's charity in earnest. By 1813 he was a governor of the Radcliffe Infirmary. At a meeting of the governors in April 1813, a proposal was made for the building of a lunatic asylum in Oxford. It was to be for those who were 'above poverty' but 'far from affluence'. The large sum of £20,000 was raised by public subscription and the asylum opened on 10 July 1826. It seems Samuel and Philadelphia each donated the sum of £200. They continued to take an interest in the project, as did Samuel's friend, the Reverend Vaughan Thomas (see later). Samuel and his sister gave a further £550 for the building of two galleries to separate violent and noisy patients from the 'quiet and gentle' ones. They gave another £1,000 for the building of a wall twelve foot high around the nine acres of the grounds so that the patients should have greater privacy. The asylum was designed to hold eighty patients and the patients were to contribute as their means allowed.

Samuel continued to give to the Radcliffe Lunatic Asylum (sometimes called the Oxford Lunatic Asylum). In 1839 the governors and subscribers of the asylum commissioned a portrait of Samuel by Thomas Phillips RA. It was a mark of their gratitude of his support 'by personal attention, judicious advice and Munificent Donation'. In 1842 Warneford wrote to Vaughan Thomas saying that he wanted the asylum to become 'a place of blessedness, I hope, to many of the afflicted of our fellow-creatures'.

Then Samuel inherited yet another fortune, this time from a cousin of his mother who died without a male heir. In 1843 he conveyed to trustees the freehold of this estate, worth in all some £1,670 per annum to the Radcliffe Asylum. Some of the money was to be used for the salary of a chaplain. Later that year the governors named the hospital 'The Warneford Lunatic Asylum' in his honour.

In 1849 his beneficence was again commemorated when a marble statue of Warneford by Peter Hollins was made for the Warneford Hospital. It can still be seen in the entrance hall. The inscription notes how his generosity allowed the asylum to 'cherish, protect and with God's blessing relieve and cure' those for whom no provision was made. The Warneford Family Arms were incorporated in the seal of the asylum. In 1851 he set up a trust so that rent from the remaining properties left to him by his maternal grandfather should be paid to the Warneford Asylum, amounting to £916 a year. The total amount of money he gave to the asylum was over £70,000.

Another major project was the building of a new hospital in Leamington Spa to replace one now insufficient. Warneford was elected onto the hospital committee in 1830 and gave generously. He was put on the building committee where he played an active role in the project. He was frustrated by delays, but he and his sister Philadelphia jointly gave £3,000 towards the total cost of £4,270 for the building, which opened in 1834. His contribution was greatly appreciated and a resolution was passed to name the hospital 'The Warneford and Leamington General Hospital'. He had not forgotten the people of Oxford though. He and his sister donated £1,500 to the new hospital in Leamington to reserve for perpetuity four beds for the use of patients from the Radcliffe Infirmary, to benefit from the waters of Leamington Spa. He took a close interest in the affairs of the hospital in Leamington, contributing to the running costs. He even threatened to withdraw his support when he learned that annual expenditure exceeded income by £11.5s.7d in the year 1839 to 1840.

Another major project was the religious education of medical students. Samuel gave over £27,000 for the founding of the Queen's Hospital and Queen's College in Birmingham. He was disturbed by what he felt to be a woeful lack of instruction in divinity for students of medicine and so in 1837 gave £1,000 to found the Warneford Prizes. These were to be awarded to candidates who wrote the best essays to demonstrate 'the pathway of God's wisdom, power and goodness as revealed by their anatomical and other studies'. The first such prize which was awarded in 1839 was for an essay on the rather surprising subject of the venous valves. The Reverend Vaughan Thomas was a trustee. Samuel instituted a similar prize at King's College Hospital in London. He put a great deal of time and effort into these projects, which amounted to something of an obsession. Indeed at times, his enthusiasm for converting the students to a Christian way of life proved something of an embarrassment to the authorities.

Samuel gave to local charities as well. The early nineteenth century was a time when poverty and unemployment were rife, due partly to the financial drain on the coffers of the Napoleonic wars. Furthermore the Enclosure Act of 1821 deprived the poor of rights such as free grazing, and many were forced to receive relief from the parish. Soon after Warneford became Rector of Bourton-on-the-Hill, the local landowner, Lord Redesdale of Batsford Park, asked for his help. Philadelphia and Samuel shared with Lord Redesdale the cost of the building and the endowment of a school in Moreton-in-Marsh for poor children of the parish.

In 1827 Samuel made 'improvements' to the church of Bourton-on-the-Hill at his own expense. It seems he was moved by the poverty of his parishioners and in 1829 he gave the site and paid for the building of a Sunday School for the instruction of 'poor boys and girls' of the parish. Two years later he built and endowed four almshouses in the village called 'The Retreat for the Aged'. It seems he was much loved by his parishioners. He established a Warneford Medical Trust to provide medical care for the poor of Bourton-on-the-Hill.

In 1834, Samuel's beloved sister Philadelphia died at the Rectory at the age of sixty-six. She had shared with Samuel in many of his projects. She was a very rich woman, having inherited quite substantial sums from various family members. She left all her estate to Samuel. It seems that at this stage, at the age of seventy, realizing that he had few close relatives and no obvious one to leave his money to, Samuel began to think about how he could best dispose of his fortune for the benefit of his fellow men. He continued to give to charities within and beyond his parish. It is interesting that he gave £200 to the Board of the Radcliffe Infirmary to pay for four beds at the Royal Sea Bathing Infirmary at Margate for the use of patients of the Radcliffe Infirmary.

Warneford's friend, the Reverend Vaughan Thomas, wrote a fond memoir of him upon his death in 1855. Warneford burned his papers and letters, but correspondence with Vaughan Thomas and others remain. They tell us much about what a remarkable man Warneford was. There were many demands on his charity. He was a shrewd businessman and kept detailed records. He always took great care to give in a way that brought most benefit to the poor, researching and travelling widely to inspect the objects of his giving. Thus, in 1818 he visited Bethlem Hospital in London to study the best way to house noisy and violent patients. He rarely missed the monthly committee meeting in Leamington. In 1838 we learn of him travelling to Eastbourne and Brighton as well as to various parts of Gloucestershire and to Monmouth. This was remarkable when one considers that this was before the coming of the railways and also that, by this time, Samuel was seventy-five years old. Often he would give in instalments so that he could adjust his giving from year to year according to how well his money was being used.

He was involved in the practical details of the projects he supported and used to say that 'doing good properly' required a great deal of hard work. In 1832 he wrote to Vaughan Thomas saying that the architect of the Oxford Asylum proposed building a 'splendid' gateway at a cost of £150. Warneford felt it would be better to use the money for reducing the fees for poorer patients: 'Plain gates and gateways must therefore I think suffice for the present'. He wrote in 1852: 'I own—as a miser—a calculating miser—that a man of taste is my terror'.

He himself lived simply and frugally at the Rectory. He travelled in a carriage that was shabby, pulled by horses that were old. Everything was geared towards the purpose of giving away the most money. Not to his family though, even the struggling parsons. He states that he 'rarely allowed himself to indulge in the exercise of private benevolence'. Not surprisingly he was not popular with his family. His giving gave him pleasure and during his latter years, when he had little close family remaining, great purpose to his life. 'I thank God for permitting me to be His humble instrument in dispensing the above'. He set up trusts, to ensure that the benefits of his charity should continue beyond his lifetime.

Returning to his family, we have little information about Margaret since the mention of her illness in 1803. There is some suggestion that she suffered from mental illness, and that it was Samuel's inability to find a home or hospital where she would be suitably cared for that led him to give his support to the building of the Oxford Asylum. We know her father died in 1822 and left money to her in trust free from 'the intermeddling of her present or any future husband'. In 1839 Margaret suffered a stroke which left her paralysed and with difficulty with her speech. A year later, on 4 April 1840, she died peacefully at home in her sixty-fifth year. She and Samuel had been married for forty-four years.

His own health began to decline. In 1841 he wrote to his friend Vaughan Thomas saying that he was virtually confined to the house owing to gout. He was gaining some relief from the new 'water dressing'. But he received 'comfort, occupation and delight' from his charitable acts. Over the following years, he continued to live a quiet life, occupied in supervising his charity. In 1853 he wrote, 'I have, indeed, great reason to bless the goodness of a merciful God, for having so far restored me, as to enable me to move on crutches'.

In October 1854, he made his last long journey, to visit his solicitor in Cirencester to discuss his will. At home he took more and more to his bed, but continued to see to his correspondence with the help of his curate. He worried about his life, wishing he had been kinder and more understanding. The description of his deathbed is moving. He was described as being like a 'small frozen bird with a tassel nightcap on his head'. A 'steam kettle was dispensing Friar's Balsam,' and 'there was a meagre fire in the grate giving out no warmth'. Samuel died on 11 January 1855 at the age of ninety-two. It was a quiet, simple funeral, the village street of Bourton-on-the-Hill lined by his parishioners and the church filled with humble mourners. There was just one carriage, that of his niece Harriet. He is buried in the churchyard there.

He had requested Vaughan Thomas to burn all his private papers. After bequests to friends and servants and various missionary societies, the residue was held in trust for his niece Lady Harriet Wetherell Warneford. The advowson of the Rectory of Bourton-on-the-Hill and

Moreton-in-Marsh was bequeathed to Lord Redesdale.

Harriet, who was childless, died in 1861. She had used the money left to her by Samuel for the Diocese of Gloucester. Some £30,000 was for repairing and purchasing churches and parsonages (this trust being set up before her death) and some £45,000 for helping impoverished clergy, widows, and orphans.

Samuel was a remarkable man, a true philanthropist devoting his life to helping those who suffered. He was devout and pious. His was a life of simplicity, totally lacking in ostentation. One is reminded of Oxford's later benefactor Lord Nuffield (see later). He also lived a simple life, taking great care to use his great wealth to do the most good to help his fellow human beings.

The Reverend Doctor Vaughan Thomas (1775–1858)

One of the wards at the Warneford Hospital is named after the Reverend Vaughan Thomas. He was an Anglican clergyman, author, and antiquarian who was influential in the building of the Radcliffe Asylum (later to be called the Warneford Hospital). He was a great friend of Samuel Warneford (see earlier), working with him in many of his projects, both in Oxford and Birmingham. He describes himself as a 'friend and fellow-labourer'.

Vaughan Thomas was born on 20 September 1775 at Kingston in Surrey. He went up to Oxford in 1792, initially to Oriel College, then transferring to Corpus Christi. He received his BA in 1796, his MA in 1800, and BD in 1809. Meanwhile, in 1803 he was elected to a fellowship at Corpus Christi. He was appointed to three lucrative livings, namely Yarnton in Oxfordshire in 1803, Stoneleigh in Warwickshire in 1804, and Duntisbourne Rouse in Gloucestershire in 1811. He held all three livings until his death and they provided him with a comfortable income. He was able to continue to live in Oxford. From 1814 he was also curate of Begbroke, north of Oxford where he took services on alternate Sundays.

In the early nineteenth century, fellows were not allowed to marry. Therefore in 1811, Vaughan Thomas resigned his fellowship in order to marry Charlotte, daughter of a Hampshire clergyman. Her brother George Williams was a fellow of Corpus and physician to the Radcliffe

Infirmary, as well as Regius Professor of Botany. Sadly Vaughan and Charlotte did not have any children.

As well as his work in medical matters, Vaughan Thomas was a formidable and ardent campaigner on all sorts of issues in the university and the Church. He was a great writer in the public papers.

The nineteenth-century Poor Law made no provision for the insane. The poor mentally ill were either left to wander as vagrants, lived in the workhouse, or were left to the 'care' of their families. However, there were privately run specialised institutions or 'madhouses' which did take in paupers as well as paying patients. These were not really medical institutions, though an honorary physician would attend to bleed or purge the patients. The violent were forcibly restrained. But the middle and professional classes were not catered for: they did not qualify for free treatment nor could they afford the fees.

The nineteenth century did, however, see a more enlightened approach towards the mentally ill and the development of public subscription asylums. This began with the opening of the York Retreat in 1796. This was a Quaker organisation which heralded 'moral treatment', a strict but humane paternalistic approach. Sanity was to be restored through self-discipline, with a simple system of rewards and punishments. Patients must dine at table and make polite conversation over afternoon tea. Moral treatment regarded exercise and relaxation in pleasant surroundings as an essential path to cure. Church services formed an integral part of the moral management.

So the governors of the Radcliffe Infirmary were inspired to expand their philanthropy and found a subscription hospital for the mentally ill of the middle and professional classes in Oxford. The idea arose with the anonymous gift of a hundred guineas for the purpose, from a Northamptonshire clergyman. The efforts of Vaughan Thomas and other enlightened individuals brought it to fruition. The governors of the Radcliffe Infirmary approved the idea in December 1812. A committee, largely men of the university, was appointed and they made a careful study of the practicalities involved. The asylum was specifically for those who had means enough that they did not qualify for help from the parish, but neither were they wealthy enough to afford care at home or in a madhouse. They would contribute on a sliding scale for their treatment and maintenance. (It is worth noting that it was not until 1846 that the Littlemore Hospital was built, following the 1808 County Asylum Act which encouraged county magistrates to provide a suitable institution for the poor mentally ill, chargeable to parishes.)

Vaughan Thomas read a paper at a meeting of subscribers soon after the opening of the hospital in 1826 which gives us a good picture of the building and the running of the asylum. It was entitled 'An Account of the origin, nature and objects of the asylum on Headington Hill, near Oxford', and was aimed at educating the public about the problem of mental illness. It reveals an enlightened and benevolent man anxious that restraint should be kept to a minimum and advocating occupational therapy and exercise. He was anxious that the asylum should not merely be a place of imprisonment and custody, but rather a place where the needy should receive help and treatment. He said that patients should not be treated 'as being deprived of their sensibilities as well as their senses'. The ill of the 'middling and inferior classes' should be given the 'comforts of a very healthy, as well as a very beautiful situation'. The site in Headington was chosen because it had room for expansion and land was cheaper than in the centre of Oxford.

Vaughan Thomas was involved in the details of design of the buildings. He designed different accommodation for different classes of patient. Thus 'parlour patients' could pay up to four guineas a week, and there would be room for a servant. These rooms subsidised less wealthy patients who paid smaller fees or sometimes nothing at all.

He was also involved in landscaping of the grounds and insisted on 'airing courts' where the patients could take exercise until they were well enough to roam freely in the extensive grounds. The grounds were adorned with trees, sundials, statues, and Grecian vases: a 'veritable Versailles'. A hired carriage could take patients into the city or the country for a change of scene. The asylum was largely self-sufficient for food and some patients helped with household duties. The spiritual needs of the patients and staff were to be met too, with prayers twice daily as well as regular services. There were all sorts of activities including cards, croquet, reading, and bagatelle. There was also a piano.

However, Vaughan Thomas's chief worry seems to be that the male and female patients should come into contact with each other! In 1834 there was a proposal for changing the use of part of the garden. Thomas was horrified that the men and women would be separated by nothing other than a low wall 'not more than six foot six and easily to be scaled'.

Vaughan Thomas was chairman of the management committee for twenty-one years and it benefitted greatly from his ability to combine meticulous attention to detail with a broad vision for the hospital. He was a shrewd man and his unflagging energy and determination to help the needy did much for the people of Oxford. It was his friendship with Samuel Warneford that led to the latter's considerable gifts to the asylum. In the early days there were not enough patients, and the governors had to resort to advertising in journals and even putting up posters! But it soon took off and the asylum had to be enlarged in the 1840s. Hundreds of patients were helped over the years. Vaughan Thomas used surplus funds to found a scheme called the 'Fund in Aid of Poor Patients', which prevented patients having to be discharged prematurely if they could no longer make their weekly payments.

Vaughan Thomas was involved in the running of the Radcliffe Infirmary too. He was a governor for many years. In the 1830s, the financial footing of the Infirmary was not too good and it was recognised that a more careful check should be made of income and expenditure. Vaughan Thomas wrote a detailed report of the Sub-Committee for the Finances of the Infirmary published in 1837.

He was also a house visitor at the Radcliffe Infirmary, enabling him to learn details of the patients' care and conditions. He passed on any complaints to the other governors. Thomas's entries in the house visitors' book reveal his interests and concerns. Again he was concerned about the moral tone of the institution and for the souls of the patients. He even scrutinised the patients' reading matter. In 1841 he saw the *Sunday Observor* in the ward, 'an abominable paper for the perusal of a sick ward'.

He held strong views about the responsibilities of parents to their children. Initially, apart from surgical cases, the Infirmary did not admit children. There is an entry in the visitors' book of 1837 in Vaughan

Thomas's hand complaining that there was a three-year-old infant on the ward suffering from burns caused by the mother's carelessness. He commented that 'This Infirmary…is made the Receptacle of Infants to save their mothers the trouble of looking after them, to the great encouragement of maternal misconduct'. It was only in 1867 that a children's ward was opened.

Just as at the asylum, he worried about the men and women mixing. When the female ward was full, some women were housed in the attics in rooms adjacent to the men's ward. Vaughan Thomas feared what would happen when they were unsupervised while the nurse went to have her lunch. He concerned himself with matters temporal too. He took an interest in the details of patient care, such as hygiene, diet, and medication.

His interest in medical matters and his great abilities in organisation and administration led to his appointment in 1832 as the Chairman of the Board of Health in Oxford. This had been formed the previous autumn as directed by the Privy Council in anticipation of an outbreak of cholera in Oxford. Over the centuries, Oxford suffered many pestilences. In fact, many colleges had rural mansion houses where the college could repair and academic life could continue undisturbed in times of danger. There were cholera epidemics in Oxford in 1832, 1849, and 1854. Despite various local and parliamentary laws over the years, the town was still susceptible because many areas were low-lying and ill-drained. The role of stagnant water, lack of ventilation, and overcrowded hovels was recognised. The cause was believed to be 'miasma' or foul air. It is interesting that at the same time Vaughan Thomas saw the epidemic as 'this fearful visitation of Divine providence'. His was very much a religious-based explanation but with some recognition of environmental factors.

Doctor John Kidd, Regius Professor of Medicine, was responsible for the medical aspects. It was a great feat of organisation, an area in which Vaughan Thomas excelled. Sewers were cleaned and inhabitants advised about cleanliness. A cholera hospital was built near the canal and a 'House of Observation' was set up in a schoolroom in St Aldate's. Here the spiritual and practical comforts of those from affected houses and streets were met. On arrival chloride solution was used to cleanse both the body and the apparel and these measures seem to have been remarkably successful as there were only five cases among two hundred and nine people admitted. Morning and evening prayers were said, including the 'Prayers to be Preserved from Cholera'. St Bartholomew's Hospital, an old almshouse in Cowley, became the 'House for Convalescents'.

Vaughan Thomas wrote an important pamphlet, 'Memorials of the Malignant Cholera in Oxford', published in 1835. It was a detailed analysis of the outbreak in which he set out how the measures adopted had contained the disease and what public health measures might be taken to prevent epidemics in the future. The official figure for the number of cases in Oxford is one hundred and seventy-four of whom eighty-six died. Vaughan Thomas sent his final report to the Central Board of Health in December 1832. The Oxford Board of Health presented him with a silver inkstand the following March.

As far as financing this great project was concerned, it was a mixture of public funding and voluntary subscriptions. Some money was raised by a rate of 6d. in the pound on rateable property. Many individuals as well as societies gave generously.

Vaughan Thomas had a paternalistic approach. He strongly believed that the poor and sick and needy should be cared for by a welfare state linked to the established Church. It should be mediated through the gentry and clergy. He termed it 'charitable jurisprudence'.

Vaughan Thomas was chaplain of Corpus Christi from 1832 to 1844. He was active in ecclesiastical and university matters, where he was an avid defender of the status quo. He was a conservative Protestant high-churchman. He was a supporter of the building of the Martyrs' Memorial in St Giles in Oxford, to commemorate the Protestant bishops burned at the stake by the Catholic Queen Mary.

He was against change within the university too. For example, he led the campaign to prevent changes to the university statutes which would have allowed Dissenters admission to the university.

Vaughan Thomas was full of good works and, like his friend Samuel Warneford, an able man of business. He was a formidable man of strong principles with very definite views. He did not allow his heart to rule his head. Thus, he felt that poor children should be educated, but only taught what was necessary for their spiritual welfare and for maintaining their station in life. Social mobility was not to be encouraged. As a justice of the peace, he was known for the severity of his sentences.

Among the fifty or so works he published was *Night March of King Charles* in 1853, the story of how Charles I and six thousand men marched silently through Yarnton to escape from Oxford during the Civil War. Thomas was a member of the Warwickshire Geological Society and presented them with fossils discovered in Yarnton during building of the railway line.

Vaughan Thomas's wife died in 1843. He then moved from his house in Holywell Street to a larger one in High Street overlooking Magdalen Bridge. He married for a second time. He lived on there until his death on 26 October 1858 at the age of eighty-three and is buried in the churchyard of St Peter-in-the-East.

Photo: The Warneford Hospital Chapel

Doctor Frederick Wintle (*c.*1803–1853)

One of the wards at the Warneford Hospital is named after Frederick Wintle, who was Superintendent of the hospital from 1828 until his death in 1853.

Frederick Thomas Wintle was baptised in Bicester on 30 March 1803. He became Assistant Apothecary at the Radcliffe Infirmary, but in June 1828 was appointed Resident Apothecary at the Radcliffe Asylum (also known as the Oxford and later the Warneford Asylum) which had opened in 1826.

All was not well at the asylum at that time as the Resident Director, Mr Moore, was not doing a good job. He had experience of working in London madhouses but was not fit for the job in Oxford and was dismissed for bad conduct. He fed the patients' veal to his dog and fattened his own pigs on hospital scraps, as well as being a poor keeper of the books.

Wintle found that the place was not without danger—from the staff as much as from patients. On 15 October 1828, soon after taking up his post, Wintle wrote to Reverend Vaughan Thomas and the Committee of Management of the asylum. He was complaining that he had suffered verbal abuse from nurse Martha Kent when he had criticised her treatment of a patient. In addition, one of the male keepers had attacked a tradesman. Wintle wanted to stay elsewhere at night, fearing for his safety.

On 28 October 1828 when the Moores had been dismissed, Wintle wrote to the Committee of Management again, explaining the sad state of affairs. He said that he felt that the services of a medically-qualified superintendent with a wife who could be matron would be beneficial to the asylum after its recent misfortunes. He even offered to marry and bring his new wife to the asylum! So, on 18 December 1828 Wintle married Jane Tustin and the two lived in accommodation at the asylum. Wintle became Resident Medical Director and ran the asylum until his death twenty-five years later.

In March 1831 Wintle was matriculated as a privileged surgeon apothecary in the University of Oxford. A 'privilegiatus' or 'privileged person' was a person who matriculated and was therefore a member of the university, although not a student. The status was granted to certain Oxford tradesmen (and college and university servants) and allowed them to claim the privileges of the university and to be exempt from certain jurisdictions of the town. Wintle was one of the last to gain this status. In the register of those who matriculated in the university he is listed as 'chirurgus et pharm.', which means 'surgeon and apothecary'. We do not know exactly what his training had been. Indeed some apothecaries also styled themselves surgeons and some privileged surgeons also acted as apothecaries. It seems he was medically qualified as well, as we do know that he became a Licentiate of the Society of Apothecaries in 1828, a Member of the Royal College of Surgeons in 1833, and a Member of the Royal College of Physicians in 1842.

Wintle's title is variably described in the records, sometimes Resident Director, sometimes Resident Superintendent, sometimes Resident Physician, sometimes Apothecary, and sometimes Surgeon to the Asylum. Be that as it may, he was really responsible for the day-to-day running of the hospital. He would be in charge of the staff which consisted of two female nurses, two male 'keepers', a cook, and a housemaid. There was a visiting physician who would be responsible for medical needs of the patients.

Frederick and Jane had seven children, six boys and one girl. One child died at the age of fourteen, but the rest survived to adulthood. One son was christened Ogle Richard after Doctor James Adey Ogle, who was a visiting physician at the hospital. Another was christened Vaughan Benjamin after the Reverend Vaughan Thomas.

The children seem to have done well and to have had musical abilities. Ogle received ten pounds a year for playing the organ at the asylum. He was a chorister at Christ Church Cathedral School, then studied at Christ Church, and later became the headmaster of a grammar school. Their son Frederick was a chorister at Magdalen College School, then entered Christ Church and took Holy Orders.

It seems that the Wintles were quite happy to bring their children up at the hospital: indeed it was a family affair. Some of the patients were allowed to mix socially with the family if it was thought to be to their benefit. One of the children ('young Mr. Wintle') became secretary to the Warneford. On his father's death, he took over the management of the male patients. When the new superintendent took over, young Mr Wintle was given rent-free rooms at the Asylum Lodge and free meals at the superintendent's table. He was also paid a small salary so that he might complete his medical training at the Radcliffe Infirmary.

Frederick died on St Valentine's Day, 14 February 1853, at the age of fifty. He had been highly regarded by all who worked with him, and the Committee of Management regretted the loss of their 'faithfull [sic], able and assiduous director'. Many patients mourned the loss of a trusted friend. He is buried in the churchyard of St Andrew's in Headington and his son Francis who died in childhood is buried in the same grave.

Frederick and Jane Wintle oversaw a period of efficient and benign management of the asylum. Frederick seems to have been a quiet man, working well with the Committee of Management. He was described by one patient as a short, dapper, neatly-suited man, always wearing garments of the finest quality. Jane seems to have been equally efficient.

The early days of the asylum in Oxford saw the tail-end of the traditional treatment of the mentally ill. The sometimes brutal regimens of the previous centuries on the one hand, and neglect on the other hand, were being replaced by the more humane and enlightened 'moral movement' (see chapter on Vaughan Thomas). This had always been the aim of the new asylum. Frederick Wintle oversaw the development of these new values in his days as superintendent.

In Doctor Wintle's time, Doctor Ogle was the visiting physician and the two men worked together. In the early days a wide variety of drugs were used, especially opiates, emetics, and diuretics. We know Wintle used arsenic and creosote. Tonics were made from steel and bark. Patients might be bled and cupping, blistering, and clystering (use of rectal injection of medicines) were all practised. Water treatments such as bathing and showering were used. In 1830 an 'electrifying machine' was purchased for the use of Doctor Ogle at a cost of five guineas.

At this time, there was provision for mechanical restraint for self-destructive or very violent patients. The accounts book reveals the purchase of restraint chairs and wrist-locks. However, mechanical restraint could only be used when the superintendent or visiting physician was present. Solitary confinement was also an option. There is no evidence that these methods were abused. Furthermore, the nursing staff increased in training and in numbers, and finally mechanical restraint ceased.

Management of the patients was, however, very much influenced by the new moral movement. Fresh air and exercise, social niceties, and religious observation were all part of the treatment. It seems that the Warneford Asylum was an enlightened and progressive place under Doctor Wintle. It offered stable care to its patients in a moderate and kindly way. It has been said that it provided a Christian way of life resembling a gentleman's household. Some patients kept in touch after they were discharged and others were happy to stay on a long-term basis as chronic patients.

Thomas Allen (*c.*1802–1873)

Thomas Allen became Resident Medical Superintendent of the Warneford Asylum on the death of Frederick Wintle in 1853, serving until 1872. His wife Charlotte was Matron. Allen Ward at the Warneford Hospital is named after them.

We know from the census returns of 1861 that Thomas was fifty-nine and had been born at Crewkerne in Somerset. He was listed as being a Fellow of the Royal College of Surgeons. He and Charlotte had two daughters, Charlotte and Mary, living with them at the asylum, both of whom were born in Oxford.

Thomas Allen was matriculated as a privileged 'chirurgus et pharmacopola' in the University of Oxford in 1831, like his predecessor Frederick Wintle. It seems that whilst an apothecary, he was not qualified as a doctor. He is listed in Oxford directories as a surgeon practising from Magdalen Street and Broad Street. So it is clear he lived and worked in Oxford before being appointed to his post at the Warneford. Indeed, he played an important role in the cholera epidemic of 1832. He took over the management of the temporary cholera hospital in Oxford and wrote two works on the subject. Vaughan Thomas was so impressed with Allen's abilities and devotion to duty that he recommended him for the post of superintendent of the asylum on Wintle's retirement in 1853.

It was an inspired choice, as the Allens continued the good work of the Wintles and ran the asylum efficiently and with care and attention to the patients. They oversaw improvements to the asylum. In 1857 Vaughan Thomas invited John Conolly, Medical Superintendent of the Middlesex Asylum, and seen as an expert in the field, to visit the Warneford Asylum. He wanted his advice on extensions and improvements to the asylum. When Allen showed him round, Conolly was impressed by the grounds and gardens. He did, however, suggest changes to the treatment of the patients in line with modern thinking. Rather than simply being a place of safe-keeping, there should be a more actively curative programme.

Among the changes the Allens oversaw were improvements to the drainage and sewerage systems, and the introduction of gas lighting in 1870. They also oversaw the purchase of five acres of land which allowed future expansion.

The couple retired in 1872. Thomas had reached the age of seventy-one and his health was failing. It was felt that his wife should retire at the same time. Their combined salaries at the time were £700, which included separate sums for their services as secretary and organist of the asylum. The Management Committee decided upon a pension of £240 per annum for Thomas and £50 per annum for his wife. When this was put to the Charity Commission, it was considered to be rather generous as a pension was usually about a third of the salary. However, when the financial situation of the asylum was considered, this amount was agreed upon. It would seem that Thomas and Charlotte Allen were highly thought of for such a generous pension to be awarded to them.

Sadly Thomas died after only a few months of retirement, on 5 January 1873. His wife survived him by many years.

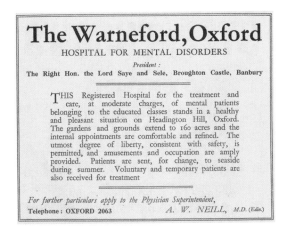

Doctor Alexander Neill (d. 1938)

Alexander William Neill was Superintendent of the Warneford from 1914 to 1938. There is a room named after him at the hospital.

He studied medicine at Edinburgh and became Senior Assistant Physician at the Edinburgh Royal Asylum. He was appointed Superintendent Physician at the Warneford in September 1914. During his time there, an assistant medical officer shared the day to day duties, and physicians and surgeons at the Radcliffe Infirmary offered their services on an honorary basis as required.

One of Neill's main contributions was to oversee the extension of the grounds by purchase of adjacent land. When he took over in 1914, the new nurses' home planned by his predecessor James Neil was opened. This coincided with an increase in the number of staff, which improved patient care.

He died on 2 May 1938. We do not know where he is buried, nor much about his life.

Photo: Nurses relaxing (1938) in what was to become the McInnes Room

Doctor Robert McInnes (1903–1987)

The McInnes Room at the Warneford Hospital is named after Robert Gow McInnes, who was Physician Superintendent of the Warneford Hospital from 1938 to 1967. He had a great influence on psychiatry in Oxford after the Second World War, modernising it and taking the Warneford and Littlemore Hospitals into the National Health Service. The McInnes Room has been a recreation room for staff and patients in its time and is now used for hospital functions.

Robert Gow McInnes (always called Robin) was born in Alloa in Scotland on 31 August 1903. He was educated at the Dollar Academy in Scotland and at Edinburgh University where he shone academically, winning many medals and prizes during his medical training. He graduated in 1927 and gained experience in various fields before specialising in psychiatry. He became Deputy Physician Superintendent at the Royal Edinburgh Hospital for Mental and Nervous Disorders where he had the care of some nine hundred and fifty patients.

It must have been a welcome change to come to the Warneford Hospital in 1938. At the time it was a small private hospital, feeling like a country house. However, he saw it through a period of great change and by the time he retired in 1967 it was an NHS hospital run jointly with the Littlemore.

All this was possible because McInnes was such an able administrator, and good at working with others. His gifts were used to good effect when the NHS came into existence in 1948. He had hoped that the Warneford could remain independent but with some financial help from the NHS; however, Aneurin Bevan said it must be one or the other. When the hospital had been founded in 1826 it had been primarily for the treatment of the middle and professional classes. Such patients were unable to pay for private treatment but were not eligible for free care at the publically-funded Littlemore Hospital. So to prevent the exclusion of these patients, McInnes together with the Hospital Management Committee decided in favour of the Warneford entering the NHS.

McInnes instigated a number of advances which changed the face of treatment at the Warneford Hospital. First, in 1949 he appointed the first psychiatric social worker. The following year, he appointed the first psychologist, one May Davidson (see next chapter), and together they built up a department of clinical psychology. He also developed occupational therapy at the hospitals. As early as 1951, he brought in open mixed wards and in the 1960s, he introduced general unlocking of the wards. He also expanded day care.

McInnes founded the Park Hospital for Functional Nervous Disorders, adapting the building which his predecessor had purchased. In 1958 he turned it into a child psychiatry and epileptic unit. He also planned the adolescent unit, although it was not opened until 1968, after his retirement.

From the 1950s, most of the mentally ill members of the university were cared for at the Warneford. There were facilities for study and examinations, so much so that it was sometimes called 'Warneford College'. It was reputed to get more firsts than any other college in Oxford.

McInnes was keen for the Warneford and Park Hospitals to be a centre for teaching and research. In the late 1960s, the first Chair of Psychiatry in Oxford was endowed. Furthermore, it looked as though the services at the Warneford and the Littlemore Hospitals would be co-ordinated forming a university department of psychiatry. He therefore felt able to retire in 1967, happy that he had left Oxford psychiatry in a good and healthy position.

Sadly his health suffered and during his twenty years of retirement, he was dogged by cardiac problems and Parkinson's disease. He was cared for devotedly by his wife Dorothy whom he had married in 1935. He died on 24 October 1987, aged eighty-four, survived by Dorothy who died in 2000, and their daughter Jane.

Thus McInnes oversaw major developments in psychiatry in Oxford. All this was possible because of his determination and wisdom assisted by a keen sense of humour. He applied himself wholeheartedly and devotedly to this cause.

Miss May Davidson (1914–1982)

The Department of Psychology building at the Warneford Hospital is named after Miss May Davidson who set up the Department of Clinical Psychology in Oxford. She was a much-loved and esteemed figure in the hospital.

May was born on 14 November 1914 in South Africa. She read chemistry, psychology, and education at the University of Cape Town. She came to this country in 1938, taking up a research fellowship in psychology at University College, London. She worked in the Operational Research Unit of the Admiralty during the Second World War before coming to Oxford as psychologist to the City of Oxford Education Committee.

Once the National Health Service was formed in 1948, May switched from educational to clinical psychology. She played a very important role, founding and setting up the service in Oxford. She worked in the Oxford region for thirty years.

She combined keen intelligence and administrative skills with a devotion and care for her colleagues and patients. She is fondly remembered for her sympathy and understanding of troubled undergraduates, supporting them and enabling them to achieve their full academic potential. She took care of those taking finals from the hospital, and would always report back to the staff on the wards how they had done. In recognition of this work, she was awarded an honorary MA by the University of Oxford in 1969.

As well as her pioneering work in Oxford, May played an important part in the development of the discipline of clinical psychology in the country as a whole. Among the many positions she held, she was the first official advisor to the Department of Health and Social Security on matters related to psychology. She was made a CBE in 1980. May also made an important contribution to the British Psychological Society. She was president in 1976/7 and chaired numerous bodies within the society.

May is remembered with affection as a charming lady by those who worked with her. She was a real character. Her office was blue with cigarette smoke, with piles of books on all the chairs.

May developed a progressive disease and retired in 1980. She faced her illness with courage and wit, not afraid to talk about dying, and continuing to find new interests and enjoyment in life as her condition allowed. She died on 5 January 1982 at the age of sixty-seven, a highly-regarded member of her profession.

Professor Michael Gelder,
Emeritus Professor of Psychiatry (1929–)

Professor Gelder was the W.A. Handley Professor of Psychiatry in Oxford from 1970 until his retirement in 1996. The Gelder Room in the Wellcome Building, part of the University Department of Psychiatry at the Warneford Hospital, is named after him.

Michael Graham Gelder was born in Ilkley in Yorkshire on 2 July 1929. He attended Bradford Grammar School and won a scholarship at Queen's College, Oxford where he took a first-class degree in physiology. He completed his medical training and did house jobs at University College Hospital in London.

His National Service was in the Royal Army Medical Corps in the NATO headquarters in Germany, where he looked after service families and became interested in the psychological problems of his patients—and began to consider a career in psychiatry.

Returning to Britain, he worked in emergency medicine at UCH and obtained the MRCP. At UCH, he was impressed by Doctor Desmond Pond, a newly appointed consultant psychiatrist—later to become Sir Desmond, President of the Royal College of Psychiatrists and Chief Scientist at the Department of Health. Michael worked as senior house officer to Doctor Pond at UCH, enjoyed this, and moved to the Maudsley Hospital where he completed specialist training in psychiatry and became interested in the then new methods of behaviour therapy. He moved to the Institute of Psychiatry and led the first randomised controlled trial of behaviour therapy. Five years later, he returned to the Maudsley Hospital as a consultant psychiatrist while continuing part time in the institute as its Vice Dean.

In 1969 Michael Gelder was appointed to the newly-created Chair of Psychiatry at Oxford. As the first holder of the post, there was much for him and his newly appointed colleagues to do. Within a short time they had developed a teaching programme for medical students, a training scheme for junior psychiatrists, a service for patients with psychiatric problems admitted to medical wards, and a programme of research. To improve the links between the Warneford Hospital, where the university department was based, and the Littlemore Hospital, a research laboratory was created in a converted ward at the Littlemore.

Professor Gelder's main research interest has always been in behaviour therapy for the various kinds of anxiety disorder. He led a series of research programmes investigating the cognitive and behavioural abnormalities that give rise to anxiety disorders, developed treatments to correct these abnormalities, and tested the new treatments in randomised controlled trials. To widen the scope of the department's research when he arrived in Oxford, Michael Gelder initiated investigations of the neuroendocrine changes associated with psychiatric disorders and their treatment. This research began as a collaboration with the Professor of Anatomy, Geoffrey Harris (see section on Churchill Hospital), and continued after his premature death with David Grahame-Smith, Professor of Pharmacology. This line of research gave rise to a succession of biochemical studies of mental illness that are continuing.

Over the years, Professor Gelder widened the scope of the department by initiating research groups on child psychiatry, old age psychiatry, and neuroscience. The teaching of dynamic aspects of psychiatry was strengthened by the appointment of Anthony Storr and Sidney Bloch, both of whom were renowned for their writings as well as for their clinical expertise.

Michael Gelder retained his interest in general medicine. He became a Fellow of the Royal College of Physicians and a Member of the

Association of Physicians. For many years he represented the university on the Board of the Oxford Hospitals. In the Royal College of Psychiatrists he was Vice-President and is an honorary fellow. For many years he served as chairman of the Neuroscience Committee of the Wellcome Trust.

There have been big changes in the practise of psychiatry since Professor Gelder began his career, especially the development of community care. Another change, and the one most related to his own work, is the present widespread use of cognitive behavioural therapy. Over the same period, research has been transformed by advances in brain imaging and genetics.

Professor Gelder has published many papers, most on behavioural and cognitive therapy. He is the senior author of the acclaimed *Oxford Textbook of Psychiatry*, written with his Oxford colleagues Dennis Gath and Richard Mayou. It is now in its sixth edition and has been translated into Russian, Chinese, and other languages. He was also the senior author of a prize-winning textbook for medical students and senior editor of the two volume reference work, the *New Oxford Textbook of Psychiatry*.

Professor Gelder retired in 1996. He is married with three children and among his interests are all things Italian.

The Nuffield Orthopaedic Centre

Photo: Dr Charles Wingfield in whose memory the original benefaction was made.

Mrs Hannah Wingfield (1789–1870)

The Wingfield Building at the Nuffield Orthopaedic Centre was opened by Sir Roger Bannister in 2004. It is named after Mrs Hannah Wingfield, the chief benefactor of the Wingfield Convalescent Home, which eventually became the Nuffield Orthopaedic Centre.

Hannah was born in Liverpool in 1789. She married Doctor Charles Wingfield who became a consultant at the Radcliffe Infirmary. They had just one child, a daughter called Mary, who sadly died in 1825 when only four years old. Hannah had a further sadness when her husband died of cholera in 1846. She lived at 54 Broad Street and the house still stands in Trinity College grounds near Blackwells.

In the 1870s the need for a fever ward in Oxford was recognised but those in high places could not agree as to whether it should be for the wealthy or for the poor. At this time, the Reverend John Rigaud stepped in. He was a fellow of Magdalen College and curate of St Mary Magdalen Church. He was on various charitable and medical committees. He proposed that the funds should be used instead for a convalescent home for patients who could not afford to pay for convalescence.

Mrs Wingfield was the chief benefactor and donated the sum of £1,545. Land was bought from Magdalen College on the corner of Windmill Road and Old Road in Headington. The foundation stone was laid in May 1871 and the Wingfield Convalescent Home was officially opened in 1872. Sadly Hannah did not live to see the fruits of her benefaction as she died on 20 January 1870 at the age of eighty-one. She was buried together with her daughter and husband in the churchyard of St Mary Magdalen, where the grave can still be seen.

Throughout the many changes to the hospital over the years, its name has changed several times. Thus in 1920 it became the Wingfield Orthopaedic Hospital, in 1931 the Wingfield–Morris Hospital, then in 1950 the Nuffield Orthopaedic Centre. It seems sad that the Wingfield name is no longer part of the hospital's title. There is still a Wingfield League to link together past and present members of staff.

William Morris, Viscount Nuffield (1877–1963)

Lord Nuffield, the man behind the Morris Motors car manufacturing business, is equally well known for his generous benefactions. These are largely in the field of medicine and include large sums of money to the University of Oxford. He founded the Nuffield Professorships, gave money for the Nuffield Orthopaedic Centre, and founded Nuffield College. There are a number of Nuffield scholarships and lectureships and a Nuffield Room at Osler House. During his lifetime, he gave away over £27 million for charitable purposes. He is included here because though not a doctor himself (though he said he would like to have been one), he has had such a huge influence on medicine in Oxford.

William Richard Morris was born in Worcester on 10 October 1877. Both his parents were well-educated, from Oxfordshire farming families. William's father, Frederick, went to Canada where he drove a Royal Mail coach across the prairies. He was even made a blood-brother in a Red Indian Tribe. On his return, he was articled to a draper in Worcester. He married and there were seven children, of whom William was the eldest. Four of the children died young. Frederick preferred the outdoor life of farming, so the family returned to Oxford in 1880 when William was three years old. William grew up in Cowley St John and attended the village school there, leaving at the age of fifteen to support the family when his father was forced to give up farming owing to illness. By then, he had already shown an interest in machinery, taking apart and putting back together the penny-farthing he had bought.

Cycling was all the rage, and Oxford was a good place for bicycles because it is flat, as well as having a huge market with the students. Following a short apprenticeship, with capital of £4, he set up his own business in 1893. He worked from a brick shed in his father's garden, repairing and hiring out bicycles and using one of the front rooms of the family home as a showroom and shop. He soon began to build bicycles too. He worked hard, travelling great distances to collect components, and sometimes working through the night. The first bicycle he built was for Mr Pilcher, Rector of St Clement's, who was a particularly large man. Each customer was measured up for their cycle and this was the largest bicycle Nuffield made. It must have been well made as William bought it back many years later at a rummage sale and proudly displayed it in his office. William was a keen amateur racing cyclist, winning many competitions.

Having outgrown his parents' shed, he rented a shop at 48 High Street, opposite the Examination Schools. Then William built himself a motorcycle and decided to produce them commercially. In 1902 he rented an old livery stable on the corner of Holywell Street and Longwall Street; you can still see the old premises. Here he garaged cars for the wealthy undergraduates who were beginning to own these new-fangled machines. He also repaired and serviced them and was soon beginning to think about building cars himself. Unlike many, he saw a future for the automobile. As the business expanded, he acquired various premises in Oxford.

In 1904, at the age of twenty-six, William married Elizabeth Maud Anstey whom he met cycling. She was a dressmaker at a department store in Oxford. They set up home opposite William's childhood home in James Street in Cowley.

William's idea was to build a car that was affordable to the masses, but at the same time reliable and inexpensive to run. His first car, the 'Morris Oxford', was produced in 1913 at a cost of £165. He purchased his components from existing companies, and assembled them in the Longwall Garage. The business was expanding so he rented and later bought an old grammar school, which more recently had been a military training college, in Temple Cowley. He lived in the adjacent manor house.

From 1915 to 1918 the factory was turned over to production of munitions and only a few cars were made. After the war, he built up the business and in 1925, he sold fifty-five thousand cars, which was 41 per cent of the national output. He inspired others to work hard too. He could be difficult to work for, autocratic and moved to anger by laziness or stupidity, but he paid fairly and was respected and loved by his employees. He provided medical services for them and special facilities for the disabled to work. He cared about the safety of his employees and his customers and was one of the first British employers to have a pension scheme.

In the 1923 general election he thought of standing as a Conservative candidate, because of his passionate belief in the importance of free trade and full employment.

The economics of the car industry are complex. Suffice it to say, the fortunes of the company fluctuated widely over the years with the changes in Britain's prosperity. Whilst driven and totally absorbed in the business in the early days, later there were times when Lord Nuffield took his finger off the pulse, being absorbed in his benefactions and public affairs. At other times he was guilty of capricious interference and failure to modernise.

Initially he owned the company himself but in 1926 he floated the company on the Stock Exchange, turning Morris Motors into a public company. In 1936, amidst great excitement in the Stock Exchange, the ordinary stock of Morris Motors was put on the market. Lord Nuffield retained a large part himself, so that he remained in control of the company. He was now in a position to increase his charitable giving. From this time on, most of the gifts to his four major trusts were in the form of gifts of shares.

With the outbreak of the Second World War in 1939, car production ceased and tanks, Tiger Moth aeroplanes, ambulances, and torpedoes were all made in Lord Nuffield's factories. They were also a centre for repair of aeroplanes, a very important task.

Lord Nuffield found the war a strain and afterwards the Nuffield

Organisation was never the same again. In 1952 it merged with Austin to form the British Motor Corporation, but only six months later Lord Nuffield retired as chairman. Production of Morris cars ceased in 1983 under British Leyland, the sad demise of a once hugely successful business. In 1929 he was made a baronet for his achievements in industry. In 1934 he was raised to the peerage, becoming Baron Nuffield and in 1938 he was made Viscount Nuffield.

After the First World War, Lord Nuffield was advised to take up golf for his health's sake and he played at Huntercombe Golf Club, in a village between Wallingford and Henley-on-Thames in Oxfordshire. The club let him rent part of the clubhouse as he found it easier to relax there, but in 1925 there was talk of the club being sold for building. Lord Nuffield therefore simply bought the golf club. A number of doctors from Guy's Hospital played there, and Lord Nuffield enjoyed their company and his discussions must have been food for thought for his future benefactions. He could always ask for advice on his many largely hypochondriacal ailments too.

In 1932 the Nuffields bought Nuffield Place in the village of Huntercombe, near the golf club. It had been designed by a pupil of Lutyens. There is a surprise when one goes into the room that was Lord Nuffield's bedroom. On opening a pine cupboard, a built-in workshop is revealed with tools and a bench and vice. If he couldn't sleep, he would repair shoes or clocks. The cupboard also contained his appendix in a glass jar! There is a lovely garden.

Lord Nuffield bequeathed the house to Nuffield College, stating that it must be kept as it was during his lifetime and used as a retreat for members of Nuffield College. The cost became too much for the college, and it was bought by the National Trust and is thankfully open to the public.

We must now consider the Nuffield benefactions. Although in Oxford we associate him with medical gifts, in actual fact he gave to a wide variety of organisations in different parts of the country and overseas. He was rather like Samuel Warneford (see section on Warneford Hospital) in that he gave much time and thought to his giving, doing careful research. Like Warneford he hated waste and felt the responsibility of his fortune. Both men lived simple and unostentatious lives and were saddened by any tendency towards 'frills'. Neither man had sought wealth. On one occasion Lord Nuffield said, 'One can only wear one suit at a time.' Having built up his wealth, it was his ambition to help those less fortunate than himself. As he did with his business, he worked by appointing the right person and letting them get on with the job, but keeping in touch and informed of major developments. He gave away some £28 million which is equivalent to £1.3 billion in 2013.

1926 saw Nuffield's first major benefaction. It was a gift of £10,000 to enable parents to visit their children in borstal. (This was somewhat ironic as years later a borstal was built next to their home at Nuffield Place and Lady Nuffield who was of a nervous disposition constantly feared an inmate would escape.)

During the Depression of the 1930s, there was great poverty and unemployment. In 1936, Nuffield put £2 million into what became known as his Trust for the Special Areas, to help industry in depressed parts of the country. Another important endowment was the Nuffield Trust for the Forces of the Crown, providing recreational facilities for servicemen during and after the Second World War.

Lord Nuffield's medical benefactions are worth enumerating in detail, partly because they are a fascinating story in themselves, and partly because they contribute much to the history of medicine in Oxford.

There is evidence that his friendship with Sir William Osler was influential in Lord Nuffield's gifts to medicine in Oxford and beyond. The Oslers bought a car (a Renault) and employed a chauffeur. The car was somewhat unreliable, and once Osler had heard that there was a reliable mechanic in the vicinity, he would 'send for Willy' whenever the car wouldn't start. The two men became friends. Morris enjoyed talking about medical topics, in particular his own problems including his indigestion. On one occasion, Osler took him into his consulting room, examined him (including giving him a blow in the solar plexus), and diagnosed a peptic ulcer. He advised him on diet and changes in his lifestyle. Lord Nuffield was rather proud of his ulcer and used to boast that it was of an unusual kind that could not be treated by ordinary means. He believed Osler had saved his life and was forever his grateful admirer.

As early as 1917, Morris, though far from being rich at this time, gave a subscription to the 'curative workshop' for which Osler made an appeal. These institutions were rehabilitation centres for the many maimed soldiers of the First World War and the one in Oxford was at the Wingfield Convalescent Home in Headington.

In 1924 Lord Nuffield was elected Vice-President of the Radcliffe Infirmary, following his generous donation of four Morris cars and two motorcycles to the hospital fundraising ballot the year before. The powers that be recognised that here was a man of wealth and vision, sympathy, and generosity, who could benefit medicine in Oxford. In 1927 he became President of the Infirmary. The Radcliffe Infirmary at that time was overcrowded and in need of modernisation. Sir Farquhar Buzzard was appointed Regius Professor in 1927, and he, Nuffield, and the new treasurer of the Infirmary, William Goodenough, made a formidable team who revolutionised the practice of medicine in Oxford and beyond.

In 1928 Nuffield led the appeal for funds for the rebuilding of the Radcliffe Infirmary, to which he himself gave generously. The following year, the plans changed: in 1929 the Radcliffe Trustees announced that they would after all be prepared to sell the Observatory and grounds adjacent to the Radcliffe Infirmary. This was because the Observatory was to be moved to South Africa where skies were clearer. By now there were murmurings of possible funding for a postgraduate school of medical research and the Observatory was seen as an ideal spot for this. So, in November 1929, it was announced that Lord Nuffield had undertaken for a sum of £100,000 to purchase the Radcliffe Observatory and grounds. The Observatory building was saved from destruction, and Lord Nuffield insisted the Observer's House be named Osler House in memory of his friend. The expansion of the Radcliffe could now go ahead on part of the Observatory grounds.

In 1930, he gave a thousand pounds to the Wingfield Orthopaedic Hospital in Headington, to help his friend, surgeon Mr Gathorne

Girdlestone (see next chapter). The hospital had started as a convalescent home then became a military orthopaedic hospital during the First World War. After the war it continued as an orthopaedic hospital for pensioners and for crippled children. Lord Nuffield gave large amounts of money for the hospital's rebuilding and development, and it became a specialised orthopaedic hospital of high repute. In 1931 it was renamed the Wingfield–Morris Hospital and in 1950 it became the Nuffield Orthopaedic Centre. Lord Nuffield continued to support it generously throughout his life and it is estimated that from 1930 to 1958 he gave well over a million pounds to orthopaedics in Oxford and throughout the world.

In 1931 the new maternity home at the Radcliffe Infirmary was opened, thanks to a gift of some £38,000 from Lord Nuffield. The home was very well liked by the new mothers. In fact, one wrote to Lord Nuffield thanking him for providing such pleasant surroundings and saying she would get pregnant again soon so that she could have another two weeks' rest!

Returning to the research institute, Lord Nuffield provided funding so that it became a postgraduate school of medical research in conjunction with the university and the Radcliffe Infirmary. It was housed in the Observatory and called the Nuffield Institute for Medical Research, opening in 1935 once the site was vacated. There were units of pharmacology and cineradiography with Doctor Gunn as director.

Professor Buzzard was pleased with the Nuffield Institute, but still had his sights set on a full postgraduate medical school. In 1935 he was therefore delighted to receive a memorandum from an Australian, Hugh Cairns, then a surgeon at the London Hospital. It was entitled 'On the desirability of establishing a complete school of clinical medicine in Oxford'. Cairns wanted an undergraduate school of some twenty carefully chosen undergraduates as well as graduates handpicked from all over the world, who would go into research. The manoeuvrings began.

In December 1935, Buzzard arranged that Hugh Cairns sit next to Sir Douglas Veale, the Registrar of the University, at a dinner. In March 1936, Cairns submitted a more detailed memorandum to Buzzard and this was circulated. Nuffield was party to the discussions that followed. On 17 July, Nuffield was introduced to Cairns at the British Medical Association meeting in Oxford. Nuffield invited Cairns to Huntercombe the next Sunday, where a small group including Girdlestone got together. On Tuesday, 24 July in his presidential address to the British Medical Association, Buzzard talked of his 'ambitious dream' for Oxford, knowing full well that it was now more than a dream, thanks to Nuffield. Three days later Nuffield saw Cairns and told him that he would give all the money required for the scheme. There were, of course, some disagreements over the details of the scheme, but things moved forward and the details were worked out. So on Lord Nuffield's fifty-ninth birthday, 10 October 1936, Lord Nuffield's gift of one and a quarter million pounds for establishing a postgraduate medical school was announced.

On 12 December 1936 a special meeting of Congregation was called in the presence of the Chancellor, Lord Halifax, so that the gift could be formally accepted and the gratitude of the university expressed. Then followed a moment of high drama. During the proceedings, a note was passed to the Chancellor who then announced that Lord Nuffield had asked to speak. The Chancellor gave permission (despite the custom that only an MA could address Congregation), Lord Nuffield arose to speak, and calmly announced that he would increase his donation to a round two million pounds (equivalent to £99 million in 2013). There was enthusiastic rejoicing.

Things then moved quickly and clinical university departments, each with a staff led by a full-time 'Nuffield Professor', were established. The original chairs and first professors were:

> Surgery (Sir Hugh Cairns)
> Medicine (Doctor Leslie Witts)
> Obstetrics and Gynaecology (Mr Chassar Moir)
> Anaesthetics (Doctor Robert Macintosh)

There was also a Nuffield Readership in Pathology (Doctor Alastair Robb-Smith).

The Chair of Anaesthetics only arose because of Nuffield's insistence, as the specialism was not seen by many as an academic one. However,

Nuffield had had experience of three anaesthetics, two bad ones and only one good. The latter had been administered by the New Zealander Dr R. R. Macintosh in London, one of the Guy's doctors who played golf at Huntercombe. Nuffield asked Macintosh if he would come to Oxford as a professor. Buzzard and the powers that be in Oxford were amazed and appalled when they learned of this. Lord Nuffield finally said all his money would be withdrawn if his wish was not granted. Thus Oxford had the first Chair of Anaesthetics in the British Empire, and it proved to be a major success.

In 1937 a Chair of Orthopaedic Surgery was added (Mr Gathorne Girdlestone), as well as Chairs of Bacteriology (Doctor Arthur Gardner) and Therapeutics (Doctor James Gunn). Finally in 1944 a Chair in Plastic Surgery was created (Mr Thomas Pomfret Kilner), the first in the country. The negotiations did not always go smoothly, with disagreements and the university and Lord Nuffield both fighting for control, but the end results speak for themselves.

These academic departments are very important in the life of a university teaching hospital, creating a link between the clinical staff and the university. They are responsible for organising undergraduate and postgraduate teaching as well as playing a part in clinical care, In addition they have the facilities and the time for scientific research. Some of the staff at the Oxford hospitals did not like the idea of these new professors whom they envisaged taking over and upsetting their work. But Lord Nuffield was concerned that the academic side should not overshadow the facilities for patient care and he continued to donate generously to the hospitals.

Whilst the Nuffield Endowment was primarily for a postgraduate medical school, in the trust deed there was provision for the possibility for a small undergraduate clinical medical school in the future. This was a controversial point as Nuffield believed the government should pay for undergraduate training. However events were hastened by the Second World War when bombing in London brought students from London hospitals to the safety of Oxford.

Two particular areas in which Lord Nuffield was interested were welfare of the blind and the care of 'crippled children'. A touching story of his munificence is his provision for every hospital in the British Empire to have an 'iron lung'. Seeing a film of poliomyelitis patients during the epidemic of 1938 he produced some seventeen hundred in his factory and saved the life of many polio patients.

In 1939 Lord Nuffield endowed one million share units in Morris Motors Limited to create the Nuffield Provincial Hospitals Trust. It stemmed from Professor Buzzard's 'ambitious dream'. Its aim was to co-ordinate hospital and ancillary services, dividing the country into regions each with a university medical school and key hospital at its centre. Having set up a similar scheme in Oxford in 1936, it was time to expand it nationwide. This project was very successful and through the board of trustees, a huge number of projects have been supported in a variety of fields, including nursing, social medicine, and industrial health centres. An important project dates from 1943 when money was given for research into and development of penicillin treatment (the preclinical departments had been upset not to receive money from Lord Nuffield's £2 million donation). The trust's role changed with the coming of the National Health Service in 1948. Another important grant was to the Christ Church Conference of 1961 led by Sir George Pickering, which paved the way for continuing regional postgraduate medical education.

There were many gifts to hospitals and medical causes outside Oxford too, especially to Guy's Hospital. There were also non-medical benefactions, one of which was the founding of Nuffield College. Lord Nuffield's dream was for a college of engineering and business which would bridge the gap between industry and academia. Lord Nuffield was disappointed when Lord Halifax, the Chancellor of the University, said that the need was rather for a postgraduate college for research in social studies. All was agreed and formalised by November 1937 and Lord Nuffield gave a million pounds. He continued to support the college financially over the years but he was always sad that his dream of a college of engineering never came to fruition.

In 1943, Nuffield gave his greatest single gift, Morris Motors stock valued at £10 million as a charitable trust to form the Nuffield Foundation. Its objects are a reflection of the interests he held dearest, and include grants, large and small, to a wide variety of pioneering projects. They were in four major fields. Firstly, the advancement of health by the development of medical and health services. This should include research and teaching, and the prevention and relief of sickness. Secondly, the advancement of social well-being, through education, improved organisation, and research. Thirdly, the care of the aged poor. Finally, the advancement of education (this was added in 1951). To take the example of old age, the foundation established the Centre for Policy on Ageing, which provided practical help for the elderly as well as funding research into subjects such as mental deterioration. It set up the first sheltered housing association in 1963. The Foundation is still a major charitable organisation and its role above politics puts it in a privileged position to approach projects with a clear eye. In 1946 he made a substantial donation of £50,000 for the founding of a national private insurance scheme which became BUPA, the British United Provident Association.

Lord Nuffield occupied the same office in Cowley for fifty years. In it were pots of pills, and the bicarbonate of soda which was his sovereign remedy for every ailment. Such was his interest in medical matters, that if an employee looked unwell, Nuffield would call him into his office, discuss his symptoms, perhaps examine a urine sample, then prescribe something from his amateur pharmacy. At home he had a medical library of over a hundred books, most important of which was Osler's textbook.

Lord Nuffield was slightly under average height, with very blue eyes. He had a sense of humour and was a good mimic. His suits were ill-fitting. Right to the end, if he passed a stranded motorist, he would stop, roll up his sleeves, and repair the car. He loved sea voyages and was a fan of Gilbert and Sullivan.

Lady Nuffield died in 1959. The couple were not blessed with children, much to their sadness. Lady Nuffield was fond of animals, and was often accompanied by her Scottie dogs. She was a keen gardener and played golf. Despite their wealth, she continued to practise economies in the home, collecting scraps from the works canteen to feed her chickens. She was of a retiring nature but supported and encouraged her husband in his projects. Lady Nuffield had her own interests and took a particular interest in the welfare of the elderly, especially of retired nurses.

After her death Lord Nuffield, who was already succumbing to loneliness after retirement from the running of the motor business, felt sad. He frequently went to Cowley to administer his numerous charities. He had not lost his kindness and spontaneity though. His friends gave a dinner to celebrate his seventy-fourth birthday and the production of the two-millionth car. He gave the car to the National Institute for the Blind and the birthday cake to the children at Great Ormond Street Hospital. The one luxury at home was his taste for expensive cigars, and he even saved pieces of string.

He became ill in 1963 with abdominal problems and after three major operations died on 22 August 1963, aged eighty-five. His ashes were interred in the churchyard of Holy Trinity, Nuffield, the little Norman church near Huntercombe Place. Simultaneous memorial services were held at St Paul's Cathedral and the University Church in Oxford on 10 October 1963. It was a great sadness to him that there was no son to inherit his title. The balance of his estate went to Nuffield College, a sum of over £3 million which is equivalent to £161 million today.

It is interesting that Lord Nuffield had three lucky escapes with his life. On a trip to America in 1914 he missed a boat which subsequently sank in a collision in the mouth of the St Lawrence River. Shortly before this, he had narrowly missed being in a lift that crashed. (One is mindful of Osler missing a train that fell off a bridge.) Many years later Nuffield was on a ship that foundered on rocks in New Zealand. It is sobering to think how different life in Oxford would have been had he not survived.

Lord Nuffield was an eccentric and complex man, but a kind one. He applied himself tirelessly to his business empire in the early days and later to his charities and was not averse to taking risks. He was always forthright and could be difficult to deal with, at times even explosive, but he never bore a grudge for long. He was really a man of contrasts: he believed in enterprise but gave his money to the poor, he loved children but had none of his own, and he made millions but did not like wealth. Like Osler his master word was 'work'. He found the life of a public figure distasteful, disliking public speaking and preferring an impromptu few words. He was an energetic, strong, and courageous character and seemingly cheerful, but actually shy, reserved, and reticent. He was always interested in others but had few close friends and certainly in later life was not a particularly happy man.

Despite all his contacts and gifts to the university and to medicine, he felt an outsider. Lord Nuffield used to say he would like to have been a surgeon, had finances allowed. But he has done more good in the world of medicine than he would have done had he been a doctor. His munificence has been vital in changing Oxford from a university little interested in the medical sciences to one rivalling any other university in the world. Medicine gave him his greatest pleasure and was closest to his heart, and for that we must be thankful.

Gathorne Robert Girdlestone (1881–1950)

The medical library at the Nuffield Orthopaedic Centre is named after Gathorne Robert Girdlestone (always known as GRG) who, when he was appointed Nuffield Professor in 1937, was the first Professor of Orthopaedics in the country. He played a major part in making the Nuffield Orthopaedic Centre the world-famous hospital it is today.

GRG was born on 8 October 1881 at Christ Church in Oxford where his father was a canon. His father later became the first principal of Wycliffe Hall, a theological college in Oxford. He was a strict disciplinarian. GRG was educated at home before continuing his education at Charterhouse. He went up to New College, Oxford in 1900 to read medicine. He did his clinical training at St Thomas's and set his sights on a career in surgery.

GRG married Ina Chatterton in 1909 and, on returning from his honeymoon, he moved to Oswestry in Shropshire as a general practitioner and surgeon. This was a lucky move because this was where the burgeoning specialty of orthopaedics was centred. It started with the Thomas family who were bone-setters, Hugh Owen Thomas being the first to train as a surgeon, practising in Liverpool. His wife's nephew, Robert Jones, carried on the tradition. The third member of the triumvirate was Miss Agnes Hunt, a nurse who set up a home for crippled children in her shed in Baschurch in Shropshire. She asked Robert Jones to tend the children. It grew to become a school and an important hospital. GRG was very impressed by the work going on there and it sparked his interest in orthopaedics.

1910 was not a good year for Gathorne and his wife. Ina had what was probably a miscarriage, and GRG had a serious motorcycle accident, resulting in severe chest injuries. The following year Ina gave birth to a stillborn girl, and sadly they did not have any more children.

With the coming of the First World War in 1914, GRG was put in charge of the Baschurch Hospital. His chest injury prevented him going overseas in the army. Robert Jones argued for specialised hospitals which he called 'orthopaedic centres'.

In Oxford, a military hospital opened in the Examination Schools, the Third Southern General Hospital. In 1915 Ina and GRG came to Oxford as GRG was made a Captain and put in charge of Ward Surgical 7 there. By 1916 he had seventy beds under his care, but this was insufficient. The committee of the Wingfield Convalescent Home in Headington offered space for this new orthopaedic centre. Huts were built in the grounds and by 1917, GRG was in charge of some four hundred beds. In the winter of 1917–18, the beds were taken by fresh casualties rather than by convalescents due to the mass injuries of the Flanders offensive.

Once the war was over, GRG could go back to treating crippled children, which was his true vocation. The Ministry of Pensions took over the Wingfield Hospital buildings from the War Office in 1919 and it was used for pensioners requiring orthopaedic treatment. However, a ward of twenty-two beds was reserved for children. The first group were admitted in November 1919 and this was the birth of the Wingfield as an orthopaedic hospital. It became known as the Wingfield Orthopaedic Hospital the following year.

GRG still saw himself very much as Robert Jones's pupil. They were fighting to ensure orthopaedics continued as a specialty now the war was over. GRG wanted to make orthopaedics in Oxford a model for the rest of the country. An important innovation brought in by GRG and Sir Robert Jones was dividing England and Wales into orthopaedic regions with a central orthopaedic hospital, such as the Wingfield. This would have links with orthopaedic departments of general hospitals in the region; in the case of Oxford, with the county hospitals of Berkshire and Buckinghamshire. Children could be assessed and treated here. In addition they developed a number of outlying clinics in smaller towns in the region. This was very forward-thinking.

In 1919 Gathorne and Robert Jones published their plans in an important article in the *British Medical Journal* entitled 'The Cure of Crippled Children. Proposed National Scheme'. They founded the Central Council for Crippled Children (CCCC). They were keen to find the causes of the crippling diseases they saw. The most common conditions were bone and joint infections largely due to tuberculosis, congenital and acquired deformities, and paralysis due to poliomyelitis.

By the early 1920s the hospital was becoming firmly established. There was a hospital school, and a workshop for crippled boys and ex-servicemen making appliances and boots and doing carpentry. There was also a workroom where crippled girls did dressmaking and needlework. The Wingfield Orthopaedic Hospital was a voluntary hospital, and it was decided that it should be independent of the Radcliffe Infirmary. Girdlestone became the first honorary surgeon and director. By 1923 it had one hundred and twenty-five beds, mainly for children but some for adults. The average length of stay was a hundred and thirty days.

GRG had the good fortune to have Miss Fan Roberts as his personal secretary. She was a well-organised and meticulous lady, but she had an exciting past. She had been a suffragette and at one stage chained herself to the railings of 10 Downing Street. She served two spells in prison for her suffragette activities.

All this time, GRG's reputation as a surgeon was growing. He published papers on tuberculosis and poliomyelitis. An operation involving pseudoarthrosis of the hip was called 'Girdlestone's Operation'. He was a skilled and innovative operator and he pioneered theatre asepsis.

It is interesting that Lord Nuffield made a donation of £500 as early as 1922 for improvements to the hospital; it was his first gift to medicine. He became friendly with GRG and his wife. Ina tells the story of how, in the summer of 1930, Nuffield knocked on the door of the

Red House, the Girdlestone's home in Headington. He handed over a cheque for £1,000 because he had heard funds were needed by the hospital. He introduced himself as Morris of the car factory. Later that year he gave more money as the hospital was in the process of being rebuilt. Its name was changed to the Wingfield–Morris Hospital. There was great excitement when the new hospital was opened by the Prince of Wales, the future King Edward VIII, in June 1933. Over the years Nuffield gave large amounts of money to orthopaedics in Oxford, in other parts of Britain, and overseas (see earlier).

Throughout this time GRG was working hard behind the scenes, but his contribution was largely unknown nationwide as he did not like to be in the limelight. He played an important role in Nuffield's donations which led to the Nuffield Professorships. Whilst not one of the original chairs, the Nuffield Chair of Orthopaedics was founded in 1937 with GRG as the first holder. It was the first Chair of Orthopaedics in the country. Orthopaedics had now received academic blessing as a surgical specialty.

In 1940 GRG resigned his professorship but remained advisor to the hospital. He was appointed consulting orthopaedic surgeon to the Ministry of Pensions and elected President of the British Orthopaedic Society the following year. At this time, GRG suffered ill health with bouts of illness resulting from his old chest injury. He continued to attend ward rounds.

During the Second World War, the Ministry of Health requested six hundred more beds in Oxford for the treatment of orthopaedic casualties. The Wingfield–Morris Hospital already had plans for expanding on land across Old Road, so the Churchill Hospital was opened under the auspices of the Wingfield. It became a US Army hospital.

The type of patient requiring treatment at the hospital was changing over the years. Rickets was a thing of the past, antibiotics were reducing the incidence of tuberculosis and osteomyelitis, leaving poliomyelitis as the main cause of admission. In addition there was an increase in the number of elderly people with degenerative conditions.

With the coming of the National Health Service in 1948, GRG

became Chairman of the Regional Orthopaedic Subcommittee. He then felt ready to retire and he and Ina left the Red House which became a home for senior nursing staff and part of the nurses' training school. They moved to Frilford Heath, a village some eight miles from Oxford. There was talk of the hospital being renamed the 'Nuffield– Girdlestone Hospital' in 1948 as the hospital really owed its origin, its expansion, and its goodwill to Girdlestone. However he opposed this and suggested it be named the 'Nuffield Orthopaedic Centre', though this did not happen until after GRG's death in 1950.

By 1950 Girdlestone was feeling his age, and noticed he was tired after a game of his beloved golf. He was diagnosed with myasthenia gravis and a thymoma of the chest, for which he was treated with radiotherapy. He died at St Bartholomew's Hospital in London on 29 December 1950 at the age of sixty-nine. With characteristic humility, he had specified that he did not want a memorial service. He was a religious man and alongside his many academic writings, he wrote 'The Hospital Prayer Book'. There is a delightful photograph of him in the garden of the Red House holding his dog Tim.

GRG was a remarkable man. His leadership led not only to a world-renowned hospital, a centre of teaching and research, but also one with a happy atmosphere, and one the staff were proud to work in. This became known as the 'Wingfield spirit'. His second great legacy was the work he did for the prevention and treatment of crippling diseases of childhood.

There are three roads named after GRG in Headington and a blue plaque on the site of the Red House which was rebuilt as staff accommodation in 2006.

Octav Botnar (1913–1998)

The Children's Ward, Children's Outpatients Unit, and the Botnar Research Centre at the Nuffield Orthopaedic Centre are named in memory of Camelia, daughter of Mr Octav Botnar and his wife Marcela. They have been generous benefactors.

Octav was born in part of the Austro-Hungarian Empire, now part of western Ukraine. He excelled in the field of business and in 1970 he founded Datsun UK (which later became Nissan UK).

Octav and Marcela's daughter Camelia sadly died in a road traffic accident in the United Kingdom. Her parents set up the Camelia Botnar Trust in her memory to help deprived young children. They have donated large sums to the Nuffield Orthopaedic Centre and also to Great Ormond Street Hospital in London.

Octav died in Switzerland in 1998 at the age of eighty-four. A portrait of Octav was unveiled at the Botnar Centre by the Duchess of Cornwall in May 2014.

Daniel Brunner (*c.*1933–1976)

Orthopaedic Ward E at the Nuffield Orthopaedic Centre is named after Daniel Brunner who was a polio patient at the hospital from 1957 to 1959. He died in 1976 at the age of forty-three.

This ward was funded by his wife Helen, who nursed him at the hospital during his illness, and by his family. There is a portrait of him at the entrance to the ward.

Lord and Lady Tebbit

The orthotics department at the Nuffield Orthopaedic Centre is called the Tebbit Centre and was officially opened in 1996. Back in 1989 an appeal was launched to raise money for a new orthotics building. Lord Tebbit became chairman of the Orthotics Appeal, in gratitude for the treatment his wife Margaret received at the hospital. She was injured in the Brighton bombing, when a bomb was planted at the Grand Hotel during the Conservative party conference of 1984. Some £1.5 million was raised and the orthotics department is now housed in the Tebbit Centre. Most of the orthoses prescribed are manufactured on site there.

Lord Tebbit continued his links with the hospital, becoming chairman of the Nuffield Orthopaedic Centre Appeal which was launched in 1996. Over £14 million has been raised so far and put to good use including new wards and a hydrotherapy pool.

In recognition of his generous help, there is a new portrait of Lord Tebbit in the Camelia Botnar Centre, unveiled by the Duchess of Cornwall in May 2014.

The Churchill Hospital

William Drake (1723–1796)

Bagot and Drake Ward, the investigation unit in the Oxford Centre for Diabetes, Endocrinology and Metabolism at the Churchill Hospital, is named after William Drake and Sir William Bagot. They were both Radcliffe Trustees, responsible for the right use of the money left by Doctor John Radcliffe.

William Drake came of an old Buckinghamshire family and became Member of Parliament for Amersham in 1746 at the age of twenty-three. He represented the town for fifty years until his death in 1796. He was a Tory, described as 'a respectable, independent gentleman', although he doesn't seem to have made much of a mark in the House. Celebrated eighteenth-century architect and builder Stiff Leadbetter designed a family home, 'Shardeloes', near Amersham for the Drake family. It was Leadbetter who designed the Radcliffe Infirmary.

William was made a Doctor of Law in 1749 at the ceremony for the opening of the Radcliffe Library. He became a Radcliffe Trustee in 1759, during Lord Lichfield's time as chairman, and so served during the period in which the Radcliffe Infirmary was being built. He was a good and conscientious trustee and only missed two meetings until 1794 when he was too frail to attend.

A ward named after him was opened at the Radcliffe Infirmary in October 1771, a year after the hospital opened. It was a four-bedded ward. On the same day an eight-bedded accident ward was opened named after Sir William Bagot (see later). Drake Ward and Bagot Ward amalgamated in 1826 and became the Accident Ward until 1920. It then became the Accident and Emergency Unit until it moved up to the John Radcliffe Hospital in 1978.

Bagot and Drake Ward was important as the only part of the Radcliffe Infirmary to be used continuously for patient care since the opening of the hospital. There is still a plaque above the door to the old ward in the Radcliffe Infirmary commemorating this. With the imminent closure of the Radcliffe Infirmary, the ward moved to the Churchill site in 2003. Staff and patients from Bagot and Drake Ward were keen for the name to be perpetuated, so the new ward at the Churchill Hospital was named thus.

Sir William Bagot (1728–1798)

Bagot and Drake Ward in the Oxford Centre for Diabetes, Endocrinology and Metabolism at the Churchill Hospital is named after Sir William Bagot, Member of Parliament for Stafford and a Radcliffe Trustee.

William Bagot was born on 28 February 1728. His father, Sir Walter Wagstaff Bagot, was a Tory Jacobite and the family had loyally served the King in the Civil War. The family seat was Bagot's Bromley in Staffordshire. Sir Walter was Member of Parliament for Newcastle-under-Lyme, Staffordshire, and Oxford in his time. He was one of the original Radcliffe Trustees, charged with the task of ensuring that the bequest of Doctor John Radcliffe was used to the good of the people of Oxford. He took part in the celebrations for the opening of the Radcliffe Library in 1749. His son William was made an honorary Master of Arts at this ceremony. William was educated at Magdalen College, Oxford and in addition to his MA degree, he became a Doctor of Civil Law in 1754.

William succeeded his father as a Radcliffe Trustee in 1768 on his father's death. He was a worthy trustee, the last to be appointed by Lord Lichfield. He was a great friend of Lichfield's successor Lord North. Indeed, the trustees' meetings were held in Sir William's house when the demands of the war with America kept Lord North away. Bagot missed very few meetings during the thirty years he was a trustee. He was a trustee during the building of the Radcliffe Infirmary, and this is why one of the new wards at the Infirmary opened in 1771 was named after him.

Sir William was also involved in the building of the Radcliffe Observatory. It was probably he who put forward the name of James Wyatt, a fashionable and brilliant young architect, to oversee Keene in the design of the Observatory.

In 1754 Sir Walter his father had vacated his parliamentary seat in Staffordshire in favour of his son. Sir William spoke frequently in the House and was said to be 'voluble in a humorous way'. He seemed to be generally opposed to change and in particular opposed the theatre and dissenters. A loyal supporter of the government, he was raised to the peerage and became 1st Baron Bagot of Bagot's Bromley in the County of Staffordshire in 1780.

William married Elizabeth St John in Wroxham in Oxfordshire in 1760. They had eight children, but suffered tragedy when three of them died of scarlet fever within three days. Sir William died in London on 22 October 1798 at the age of seventy. Lady Bagot lived on until 1820.

See article on William Drake for details of the history of Bagot and Drake Ward.

Sir Winston Churchill (1874–1965)

During the Second World War, the Churchill Hospital was opened for the treatment of air raid casualties. It then became a United States Army Hospital. It was opened as the 'Churchill Hospital', in honour of the Prime Minister, by the Duchess of Kent in January 1942. When the Americans left, the hospital became the responsibility of the Committee of the Radcliffe Infirmary and patients began to arrive in January 1946.

Lady Churchill visited the hospital to meet staff and patients, wearing a splendid hat.

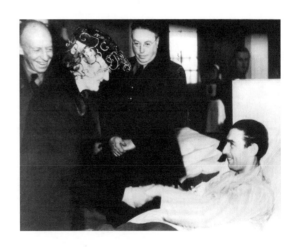

Sir Michael Sobell (1892–1993)

Sobell House, the hospice on the Churchill Hospital site, is named after the philanthropist Michael Sobell. He made a major financial contribution to the building of the hospice which opened in 1976.

Michael Sobell was born on 1 November 1892 in Galicia in Eastern Europe. His father owned factories in the Austro-Hungarian Empire and had oil interests in Germany, but the family emigrated to Britain in 1899 when Michael was seven. He was brought up in London and left school at sixteen, setting up a business making and selling leather goods. However he made his fortune as a pioneer in the electronics industry, initially making radio receivers, then television sets. His company merged with the General Electric Company, of which he became chairman in 1961. He was knighted in 1972.

He was a keen owner and breeder of racehorses, his horses winning many of the most prestigious flat races at home and abroad.

The need for a hospice in Oxford was recognised in the early 1960s, but funds were not available. In 1972 a report was written outlining the needs. Michael Sobell was President of the National Society for Cancer Relief at the time (which later became the Macmillan organisation) and he offered to fund the building of the hospice. The actual running of the hospice was to be met by the National Health Service and a charity, what is now called the Sobell House Hospice Charity.

His philanthropy was wide-ranging. The Sobell Foundation was established in 1977 making grants to a variety of projects, particularly for children, the disabled, and the elderly. These included another hospice (at Northwood in Middlesex) and a number of schools, leisure and sports centres, and community centres.

Sir Michael died on 1 September 1993 at the age of a hundred. He is buried in Willesden United Synagogue Cemetery in Greater London. He donated most of his fortune to charity.

Doctor Alastair Robb-Smith (1908–2000)

The Robb-Smith Education Centre at the Churchill Hospital provides social as well as educative facilities for clinical medical students. It is named after Doctor Alastair Robb-Smith who was, among a whole host of interests, a noted pathologist and medical historian.

Alastair Hamish Tearloch Robb-Smith was born on 11 April 1908. He lost his father on Flanders fields in the First World War, in which he was in the Royal Army Medical Corps. He had been a general practitioner in Chislehurst in Kent. The family was left in financial difficulty, but Alastair won an entrance scholarship to Epsom College.

From there he went on to study medicine at St Bartholomew's in London. He qualified in 1930 and became house physician to Gwyn Macfarlane (under whom he later worked in Oxford). He then moved into the field of pathology and began working on lymphomas. He won a travelling scholarship enabling him to visit Germany and Madrid. He showed promise early on, winning the gold medal for his London MD.

He was invited to Oxford as the first Nuffield Reader in Pathology and head of the department in 1937 at the young age of twenty-nine. It was an exciting time in Oxford as it was at the time when Lord Nuffield was endowing the new clinical chairs (see section on Nuffield Orthopaedic Centre). The new professors and readers were not universally welcomed by those who termed them 'Nuffield interlopers', but Doctor Robb-Smith weathered the storm and became a valued member of the new clinical school. He encouraged close contact and collaboration between the clinical doctors and the pathologists. He achieved world renown as a pathologist, his own academic field being the study and classification of the reticuloses. Students found his lectures inspiring, full of history and philosophy, sometimes paying little attention to the requirements of the syllabus.

Alastair took a keen interest in the various activities of the clinical students, not least in instigating the pantomime which he suggested be called 'Tingewick' after Nicholas Tingewick who was the first teacher of medicine in Oxford (see section on John Radcliffe Hospital).

Alastair had many and various interests, among them a keen interest in the history of medicine in Oxford and beyond. Even as a medical student he became an avid collector of second-hand books, not least among them those on the history of medicine. He was particularly interested in Sir William Osler (see section on John Radcliffe Hospital) and was an active member of the Osler Club of London. He received the rare distinction of being elected an honorary member of the American Osler Society in 1987 and knew many of its leading lights. In 1990 he gave the Osler Oration at the Royal College of Physicians and it was a great success, despite the fact that by this time he had little sight left. The subject was 'Osler's Changing Influence'.

He bequeathed his extensive collection of papers connected with Osler to 13 Norham Gardens where they have been catalogued and are available for study. They cover every aspect of Osler's life and career. Many of the letters are in Robb-Smith's hand, legendary as being nigh on impossible to read and once described as 'resembling the illegible gyrations of an inebriated spider'. A delightful touch is the way when dating his letters he would add that it was some Saint's day or the anniversary of some historical event. This was an illustration of the breadth of his extraordinary historical knowledge.

After his retirement his correspondence must have taken up a huge amount of time without the aid of emails and word-processing. Studying his papers one feels he was rather like a terrier getting his teeth into something, not willing to let it go until he had got the information he sought. One example is his research into the exact process by which the Regius Professor is appointed. In 1987 he corresponded with the Registrar at Windsor Castle about the procedure for the issue of the Letters Patent. He also wrote to the Crown Office at the House of Lords which supplied his request for a picture of the red leather pouch in which the Letters Patent are dispatched. His papers are full of all sorts of interesting correspondence of this kind.

Further papers were rescued when Alastair's wife died in 2006 and their house was cleared. There were two shelves of papers with a scribbled note saying they were to be given to Green College. Among them were some useful archives of the Radcliffe Infirmary as well as the deeds of the house and £5,000 of National Savings Certificates! A lucky escape from the incinerator.

Alastair had married Peggy Pickles in 1950. She was a pathologist too (although originally a botanist) and did important work on foetal death due to rhesus incompatibility. They had one daughter, Jessamy Elesaidh Janet.

Peggy and Alastair were a hospitable couple, entertaining many from all over the world, and always providing good food and wine. Their home, 'Chaucer's House' in Woodstock near Oxford, had connections with Geoffrey Chaucer's brother. Peggy retained her interest in botany and spent some twenty years breeding every type of daffodil. Alastair was Mayor of Woodstock for a while.

A somewhat surprising interest in his younger days was motor racing. He even raced his sports car at Brooklands until it was said 'to have passed under, rather than by the side of, a large meat lorry at Smithfields'. It is hard to imagine a man of more diverse interests.

In 1970 Alastair published *A Short History of the Radcliffe Infirmary* to mark the bicentenary of the opening of the hospital. It is eminently readable and full of detail about medicine in Oxford including the characters important in its history. Indeed he wrote extensively both in the fields of pathology and medical history.

Alastair died on 17 January 2000 at the age of ninety-one. The loss of his sight for the last years of his life must have been a great sadness for one with such a love of books. However, he didn't let it hinder his enthusiasm for life. He is remembered as a true polymath, but equally importantly, as a kind and considerate man, and modest despite his great talents and achievements.

Doctor John Warin (1910–1990)

John Warin was Medical Officer of Health in Oxford from 1948 to 1974. He was also consultant in infectious diseases and clinical lecturer to the university. The Infectious Disease Ward at the Churchill Hospital is named after him.

John Fairbairn Warin was born on 2 September 1910 in North Yorkshire. He was educated at Tadcaster Grammar School where his father was a teacher of chemistry. He then moved on to St Peter's School in York before studying medicine at Leeds University. Here he excelled at sports, in particular hockey and sprinting for which he represented the university.

He qualified in 1933 and after various jobs in Leeds, he became Assistant Medical Officer of Health in Blackburn in 1937. He then spent the war years in Birmingham where he was involved in organising the emergency hospital services during the Blitz.

After a short spell back in Leeds, he arrived in Oxford in 1948 as Medical Officer of Health. The Medical Officer of Health was a government official responsible for public health medicine, leading a team of public health professionals such as environmental health officers and public health nurses. His appointment coincided with the beginning of the National Health Service.

It was an important and exciting time, and it fell upon Warin to implement the public health provisions of the NHS Act. There were to be health centres unifying the medical and allied services to treat people in their homes. Warin played an important role in encouraging financial support for these centres from the local and regional health committees. This included continuing funding for staff to support the doctors, such as nurses and receptionists.

His next contribution was to persuade the general practitioners and community nurses in the health centres to become responsible for prevention as well as treatment for the patients in the catchment areas. In the 1960s, Oxford was a pioneer in the field and by the time Warin retired in 1974, there were eight health centres in Oxford which met the needs of most of the population.

Under Warin's leadership, Oxford excelled in the fields of child health and maternity services. It had the lowest infant mortality rate in the country and the highest immunisation rates for children for polio, diphtheria, tetanus, and whooping cough.

He understood the importance of representing the cause of public health on national and local boards and committees. He was skilled at obtaining funds for his causes, so much so that he was called 'that wily old fox' by a city treasurer.

His role in both hospital medicine and community health was a great advantage, a benefit to them both. He would pursue his objectives with vigour, but always showed respect for others, be they patients or colleagues. He stood the public health service in Oxford in good stead when there was pressure on funding during reorganisation of the NHS in the 1970s. He set an example to the doctors working in his department, many of whom became Medical Officers of Health themselves.

He married fellow Leeds graduate Elizabeth Simpson Bruce in 1936. They had two sons and two daughters. One son was a consultant dermatologist in Exeter. Though always loyal to his Yorkshire roots, he threw himself into Oxford life, particularly in Iffley where he lived. He died on 14 November 1990 at the age of eighty.

Warin was the last of Oxford's Medical Officers of Health, and it is interesting that over a period of a century, the post was filled by only four men. Warin had a great influence on medicine in Oxford, serving its people for over a quarter of a century.

Professor Geoffrey Harris (1913–1971)

Geoffrey Wingfield Harris is seen by many as the father of neuroendocrinology. He was the Doctor Lee's Professor of Anatomy at Oxford University from 1962 to 1971. The medical ward specialising in respiratory medicine, diabetes, and endocrinology at the Churchill Hospital is named after him.

Geoffrey Wingfield Harris was born in London on 4 June 1913. His father was a physicist who, after academic beginnings, had an important job in ballistics at Woolwich Arsenal. Geoffrey attended Dulwich College. His interest in science began here, and he even asked the headmaster if he might use the biology laboratory for dissection on half-holidays.

He went up to Cambridge in 1932 to read Natural Sciences at Emmanuel College. Here he shone academically, gaining first-class honours in parts I and II of the Natural Sciences Tripos, being elected Senior Scholar, and winning many prizes. He was awarded the Marmaduke Shield Studentship in Anatomy for 1935/6. Even at this stage he was considering the functioning of the pituitary gland, a subject that was to exercise him throughout his career. His first three scientific papers were written at this time, all on the topic of the pituitary and secretion of sex hormones.

Geoffrey married Georgina Birnie in 1936 and they had a son who, with his father's encouragement, studied medicine and became a GP.

Sadly the marriage did not last.

Geoffrey did his clinical training at St Mary's, qualifying in 1939. Whilst there he won prizes in a variety of subjects. He continued his research and wrote several papers, and did his house jobs at Hillingdon County Hospital.

From 1940 to 1952 he worked in Cambridge again. He was initially Demonstrator in Anatomy and then in 1947 he was promoted to University Lecturer in Anatomy. The following year he transferred to the physiology department as he felt a knowledge of physiological techniques was essential for his research. Initially he worked on the posterior lobe of the pituitary. His publications at this time reveal his resourcefulness, his technical skill, his patience, and the critical attitude that were the hallmarks of his career.

He soon switched to the study of the anterior lobe of the pituitary gland. This stemmed from an earlier interest in the patterns and cycle of breeding in animals.

It had been postulated that a portal vascular system might be important in the flow of humoral agents between the hypothalamus and the pituitary gland, which would control the secretions of the anterior lobe of the pituitary. It was Harris, however, who really established this in the late 1940s and early 1950s through a series of meticulous and ingenious experiments.

In 1949, using india ink in rats, he demonstrated that blood flowed in the direction of hypothalamus to anterior pituitary through veins in the pituitary stalk and thence into capillaries in the anterior lobe.

He worked with Doctor (later Professor) Dora Jacobson of Lund and they published three important papers in 1950, 1951, and 1952 in which they provided evidence for the theory. A milestone was a series of experiments in rats which involved transplanting the anterior lobe of the pituitary gland to another part of the body. Production of hormones from the anterior lobe ceased, but resumed once it was returned to its original position, but only when the original blood supply was re-established. Thus, it seemed chemical agents produced in the hypothalamus passed down the portal vein to the anterior lobe, controlling secretion of pituitary hormones.

From the time of these studies, the race was on all over the world to identify the peptides which Harris's theory postulated were produced by the hypothalamic neurones. In particular, Harris sought to identify the molecular nature of the ovulatory signal. This work occupied him for the last twenty years of his life.

In 1952 he moved to the Maudsley Hospital in London to continue his research. Growing realisation of the links between psychiatry and endocrinology had led to the founding of the Institute of Psychiatry in 1948. Through a chance meeting, Geoffrey was asked to be head of the new department. Conditions were somewhat cramped and primitive, but this did not hinder Geoffrey's work nor dim his enthusiasm. He was soon made Fitzmary Professor of Physiology of the University of London. Always interested in clinical aspects of endocrinology, he was honorary consultant at the Bethlehem Royal and Maudsley Hospitals from 1956 to 1962.

He began to turn his attention to the thyroid gland, which is under the control of the anterior pituitary gland. He showed that maintenance of normal thyroid size in rats was dependent on the integrity of the portal vessels. In 1955 he wrote an important monograph, 'Neural Control of the Pituitary Gland', in which he described his research and his theories, though at the time the mechanism was still not clear.

In 1962 Harris was invited to Oxford as Doctor Lee's Professor of Human Anatomy, and fellow of Hertford College. His predecessor Sir Wilfred Le Gros Clark had done much to rescue the anatomy department from the doldrums. Under Harris it went from strength to strength. However, there was virtually no interest in endocrinology. The Medical Research Council agreed to set up a neuroendocrinological unit in the department, and Harris was the Honorary Director. He invited scientists from all over the world to work with him. The department was also involved in clinical research and drug trials.

The race for Harris's long-postulated peptides was won by the Americans who had great drive and almost unlimited finance behind them. In 1969, the first was identified, namely TRH (thyrotrophin-releasing hormone), a small peptide which stimulates the secretion of thyroid-stimulating hormone by the anterior pituitary gland. Then came gonadotrophin-releasing hormone (GnRH). This peptide stimulates the secretion of luteinising hormone and follicle-stimulating hormone by the anterior pituitary gland, and so helped answer Harris's long quest for the mechanism of the control of reproduction.

His theory that a wide range of endocrine glands was under the control of the central nervous system had finally been proved. Whilst in Oxford, Harris continued his work on sexual differentiation of the brain. He showed that there were differences between the male and female hypothalamus and that this was hormone-induced.

His work had practical applications, for example the use of gonadotrophin-releasing hormone as a chronic pituitary suppressant in prostatic cancer, precocious puberty, and endometriosis. He was an honorary consultant at the Littlemore Hospital, running a metabolic ward. He worked with the Professor of Psychiatry, Michael Gelder (see section on Warneford Hospital), and with Sir John Stallworthy, Professor of Gynaecology, studying the effects of phenothiazines on the endocrine system and also hormone changes during the menstrual cycle and in anorexia nervosa.

Harris's success was partly due to his formidable intellect and great imagination, but also to his great practical skill as a researcher. He was always careful and sometimes cautious in his conclusions. Whilst kind and encouraging and always happy to explain experimental techniques to the young, he expected high standards from those who worked for him. His own meticulous laboratory notes and papers are in the Special Collections of the Bodleian Library. His academic achievements were immense, step by careful step elucidating the control of the many activities of the pituitary gland and studying the reciprocal interactions of the brain and endocrine glands. He was a patient man in every area of his life. He was kind and generous to others, quiet and unobtrusive.

During Geoffrey's time in Oxford there were major changes in the preclinical course for students. He played a major part in its reorganisation and ensured that anatomy was well represented in the new Physiological Sciences Honours School. He encouraged the use of new teaching methods and also integrated the teaching of histology and anatomy. Under his auspices, anatomy became one of the most popular preclinical subjects. Endocrinology became an option in the Final Honours School.

Geoffrey was a good teacher and his lectures were popular. He was keen for students to be listened to, encouraging regular meetings between staff and students. He took an active part in college politics and administration at Hertford College, and even became college librarian. He won many prizes and awards and was elected a Fellow of the Royal Society in 1953.

Geoffrey excelled at rugger and boxing in his younger days, and was an excellent senior member of the University Squash Racquets Club. In his later years he kept fit felling trees and sawing logs at Campsfield Wood, his home near Oxford. He loved travel, visiting and lecturing all over the world.

He was a great family man, and had two daughters from his second marriage. Sadly, he died on 29 November 1971 at the age of only fifty-eight.

Jane Ashley (1939–1995)

The Jane Ashley Centre is part of the Churchill Cancer Centre. It was founded by Neil Ashley in 1996, in memory of his wife Jane who died at a young age from breast cancer in 1995. The new centre opened in 2009 and consists of twenty beds, looking after women receiving surgery or radiotherapy for cancers specific to women. It aims to provide a caring, supportive, and holistic approach beyond that which the National Health Service alone can give, but at the same time to provide the most up-to-date therapy. There is a garden outside the centre where patients and their families can relax.

The family also set up the Ashley Charitable Trust in 1995, which supports a whole range of projects in the field of breast and gynaecological cancer and works closely with the Oxford Radcliffe Hospitals Trust. The projects include research into clinical treatment, promotion of patient care and comfort, education for the medical profession, and help for parents and children to aid communication at this difficult time. The family is still actively involved as trustees.

There is a portrait of Jane in the centre.

Jean Tarver

The Dialysis Unit at the Churchill Hospital is named after Jean Tarver, who was the first patient to be treated by haemodialysis in Oxford. She received treatment from 1967 to 2001.

Old Road Campus

The recently built Old Road Campus, on the site of the Churchill Hospital, houses various University of Oxford research departments. These have close links with the Oxford hospitals and its close proximity enhances the integration of scientific research and patient care.

Professor Edward Jenner (1749–1823)

The Jenner Institute for Vaccine Discovery in the University of Oxford is located in the Old Road Campus Research Building on the Churchill Hospital site. It is named after Edward Jenner who was responsible for saving millions of lives by developing vaccination against smallpox. He is the father of the science of immunology. Smallpox, caused by the virus variola, was the most feared and greatest killer in Jenner's time; he called it the 'Speckled Monster'. Those who survived the disease were left with disfiguring scars and were often blind. Women tried to hide their scars with beauty spots or veils. It is believed to have killed Prince William, heir to Queen Anne, when he was eleven years old (see article on Doctor John Radcliffe).

Edward Jenner was born on 6 May 1749 in Berkeley in Gloucestershire. The Jenner family were gentry, who had owned land in the area for centuries. Edward's father was a clergyman. Edward was one of nine children but sadly his mother died when he was young.

At the age of eight he went to a grammar school in Wotton-under-Edge in Gloucestershire. It seems there was a local outbreak of smallpox while he was there, as we know he was inoculated against the disease by a local surgeon. The method in which matter from a smallpox lesion from a patient with a mild form of the disease was injected or dried lesions were sniffed was called 'variolation'. It involved a terrible regimen, lasting six weeks. First Edward was bled and purged until he was emaciated and feeble. He was on a sweet, small diet. Then material from a smallpox lesion was injected into his arm and he was taken to an 'inoculation stable' with other artificially infected boys until the disease had run its course. He escaped with a mild form of the disease, but it was a terrible price to pay and had a lasting effect on his nerves.

The variolation regimen came to this country in the 1720s thanks to Lady Mary Wortley Montagu, a great beauty who was scarred by the disease. She had lived in Constantinople (Istanbul) and in 1721 had her son variolated. When she returned to this country, her daughter was variolated too. Three members of the Royal College of Physicians came to visit the child, and for the first time there was publicity about the technique in the press. Some of the Royal Family were variolated too, which increased its popularity. Many surgeons built up a lucrative practice performing variolation. However, death following variolation was not uncommon although much less common than that following naturally acquired smallpox. This was between 1 in 5 and 1 in 8, although in an epidemic it could reach as much as 40 per cent.

In 1746 the London Smallpox and Inoculation Hospital was founded to help patients with the disease both naturally acquired or following inoculation. In 1754 the Royal College of Physicians announced their formal support for variolation. A less severe regimen was used and it became more accepted, as well as cheaper as it meant less time was required off work.

Back to Jenner's childhood: when he was nine he moved to a school in Cirencester. It is said he had little motivation and really only showed an interest in fossils and natural history. At the age of twelve he left and became apprentice to a surgeon in the local town of Chipping Sodbury, remaining with him for six years.

It was while here that he made the observations for which he later became famous. He knew of the old wives' tale that if a milkmaid caught cowpox, it gave her lasting protection against smallpox. This virus caused vesicles on the cow's udders, and when contracted by a human, caused a mild illness and vesicles or 'pocks' on the hands.

In 1770 Jenner went to London to work under the famous surgeon John Hunter. It was a good training as Hunter was a proponent of the method of experiment and observation. Edward enrolled as a student at St George's Hospital where Hunter was Chief Surgeon. Jenner stayed at Hunter's house, and they became lifelong friends. He studied medicine as well as surgery, so that when he returned to Berkeley two years later, he was better qualified than anyone else in the area. His practice covered an area of some 400 square miles and he treated patients with all sorts of conditions. There was an accepted pharmacopoeia, and treatments included herbs and minerals. There was little actual surgery because of the problems of infection and pain.

Jenner's thoughts turned again to cowpox and smallpox. In 1796 he did an important experiment. Milkmaid Sarah Nelmes consulted Jenner about a rash on her hand and Jenner diagnosed cowpox rather than smallpox. She confirmed that her Gloucester cow Blossom had recently had cowpox. So Jenner transferred material from a pustule on her hand to eight-year-old James Phipps, the son of his gardener. It involved making two half-inch incisions in the boy's arm and dipping a clean lancet into fluid from a lesion on Sarah's hand. This was transferred into the incisions. The boy developed a pustule at the site and mild fever and lassitude but soon recovered. This experiment was notable as it was transfer of material from human to human. It was a success. The boy was variolated with smallpox material six weeks later and had no response, nor did he contract smallpox on subsequent occasions when his immunity was tested. Jenner published his discovery in 1798 in his *Inquiry into the Causes and Effects of the Variolae Vaccinae; a Disease Discovered in some of the Western Counties of England, Particularly Gloucestershire, and Known by the Name of Cowpox*. He had to publish it privately as the Royal Society was not interested. However, the stir it caused all over the world transformed him from unknown country doctor to one celebrated on the world stage. He gave the rest of his life to perfecting and publicising his technique. The term 'vaccination' was invented in 1803.

Jenner was said to be a dapper man wearing the latest fashion, his manner polished by John Hunter's wife. He was welcome in the drawing rooms of the gentry and sang in a local group. He had many friends locally and was a generous man. He was invited to go into partnership with John Hunter and to take up positions abroad, including one with Warren Hastings in India, but he wanted to stay at home in Gloucestershire. In 1788 he had married Catherine Kingscote, a local lady whom he had known for years. He was then thirty-eight. They had two sons and a daughter.

Only a week after his wedding, Edward read a paper at the Royal Society on the behaviour of cuckoos, having worked with the famous naturalist Joseph Banks on this subject. He was elected Fellow of the Royal Society the next year. With the Earl of Berkeley, Jenner went up in a hot air balloon, the first flight in Britain and some five years after Montgolfier's flight. It seems he did it for fun, though it was probably for scientific research as well. Edward founded a local medical society, one of the first provincial ones in the country. He purchased the degree of Doctor of Medicine at St Andrews University. He started to visit the town of Cheltenham frequently, and indeed it became his second home. It was a fashionable watering place and he met King George III there.

The future with regard to vaccination was, however, difficult and full of controversy, the 'antivaccinists' citing all sorts of reasons why the practice should be outlawed. Some doctors feared the loss of income due to the fall in variolation. Others pointed out that vaccination was not 100 per cent successful, but Jenner showed this was because only certain types of cowpox confer immunity to smallpox. In other cases, serious illness followed, usually because the cowpox vaccine had been contaminated by smallpox virus. Yet others objected to humans receiving vaccine that originated from one of God's lowlier creatures.

However, thousands were vaccinated at home and abroad. In 1802 Jenner purchased a house in London to set up in practice there. There was increasing support for vaccination. The Royal Jennerian Society was formed and there was a great deal of publicity. The society received royal patronage and the support of the archbishops. In 1807 the Royal College of Physicians submitted a report to Parliament strongly recommending vaccination.

It seems Jenner could be kind and generous, helping his friends, but he was somewhat naïve and self-destructive. He was passionate about his cause and gave a great deal of time to it, so much so that Parliament gave him a grant to cover his expenses. He had pioneered the method of arm-to-arm vaccination, transferring liquid from a cowpox lesion on one person to the arm of another. However, as cowpox was not a widespread disease, he developed techniques for preserving material from a human cowpox pustule dried on a thread or on glass so that it could be transported.

The National Vaccine Establishment (NVE) was founded in 1807 to promote vaccination programmes. It organised vaccination in the army and navy, offered free vaccinations at vaccination stations, opened dispensaries, circulated handbills, and wrote letters to doctors and the clergy. The old method of variolation with all its hazards declined (and indeed was forbidden by law in 1841). Jenner was elected Director of the NVE, but soon resigned after disagreements and began to isolate himself from the medical fraternity in London. He retired from Cheltenham life too for a while and spent more time in Berkeley. Whilst still practising medicine, he became a magistrate and resumed his interest in geology and fossils. At this time, his elder son Edward died of consumption aged twenty-one.

Not surprisingly, with his son's death and the controversy over vaccination, Jenner began to suffer from stress and depression. His main complaint was of tinnitus, sensitivity to noise, and a heaviness in his head, as well as dyspepsia and palpitations. He was cupped, calomeled, salted and purged, blistered, and given the water cure, but to no avail. He must have worried about his wife too as she was unwell.

He rallied somewhat and he was busy in Berkeley, performing many vaccinations as well as treating the sick. A forty-eight page volume of household medicine by Jenner called 'Directions and Observations' survives, written out by a friend and arranged alphabetically. It was aimed to help parents. The section 'Head–Blows in' is remarkably sensible, the advice being to observe the child and if he becomes sick or appears stupid, to call in a surgeon.

During the Napoleonic wars, it was common practice for prominent people on both sides to seek the release of prisoners of war. When Jenner wrote to Napoleon in 1803, legend has it that Napoleon replied 'Ah, Jenner, je ne puis rien réfuser à Jenner' (Ah, Jenner, I can refuse him nothing). At this time Jenner moved among higher circles, meeting the Tsar of Russia and the King of Prussia.

His wife Catherine died in 1815 and this led to another period of depression. Despite increasing numbers of vaccinations in the country, records showed that smallpox still occurred with varying incidence, and this upset Jenner too. There is an interesting comparison to the recent controversy over the MMR vaccination: as smallpox became less common, the fear of this dreadful disease dwindled, and fewer people came forward for vaccination.

By now Jenner was a wealthy man. He owned a carriage and when his daughter Catherine married, he gave her over £14,000.

In 1823 a servant found him collapsed on the floor in the library. It was a stroke, with paralysis of the right side. He was given the usual treatments including cutting of the temporal artery to induce greater bleeding. He died on 26 January 1823. It was very snowy on the day of the funeral. This was perhaps why no one from London came, but it was sad. He was buried beside the altar in Berkeley Church, beside his wife and eldest son.

In 1858 a statue of Jenner was erected in the newly designed Trafalgar Square, but there were protests, a country doctor being deemed unworthy to stand among the admirals and generals. The statue was removed and is now in Kensington Gardens.

Smallpox vaccination became compulsory in Britain in 1853, and in 1967 the World Health Organisation launched a campaign to eradicate smallpox worldwide. In 1980 it formally declared, 'Smallpox is dead.' It was Jenner who laid the foundations of vaccination, which has been responsible for saving more lives than any other idea before or since.

Edward Jenner's house in Berkeley in Gloucestershire is open to the public.

Sir Henry Wellcome (1853–1936)

Three buildings on the Old Road Campus at the Churchill Hospital—the Henry Wellcome Buildings for Genomic Medicine, Molecular Physiology, and Particle Imaging—are named after Henry Wellcome, pharmaceutical giant, collector, and philanthropist. There is also a Wellcome Unit for the History of Medicine on the Banbury Road in Oxford.

Henry was born on 21 August 1853 in a log cabin in a forest in Wisconsin in America. He came from a poor family, his father being a farmer. The family moved to Minnesota in 1861 because of failure of the potato crop. He was a high-spirited boy and had an exciting outdoor life, exploring the nearby lakes by canoe, and riding and shooting in the woodlands and prairies. Soon after the family's move there was an Indian uprising against the settlers, led by Little Crow. The Indians were defeated, but Henry's sense of fairness could see the injustice to the Indians and he later supported a mission to the American Indians.

The family were deeply religious, several members including his father being ministers of the Second Adventist Church. They instilled in Henry the Protestant work ethic and were ardent supporters of the temperance movement.

Henry's interest in medicine began when he was thirteen, when he left school and worked in the drugstore owned by his uncle, who was a physician. He was at home here among the accoutrements of the chemist, making up his uncle's prescriptions. He accompanied his uncle on his rounds and saw him dress wounds and splint fractures.

In 1870 he moved to Rochester, where a family friend, Doctor William Worrall Mayo, helped him find a job in a drugstore. Mayo taught Henry physics and chemistry and encouraged him to train in pharmacy, rather than spend his life in a small-town drugstore.

He therefore went to Chicago College, but when it was destroyed in the Great Chicago Fire of 1871 he moved to Philadelphia, where he became an apprentice and attended evening classes at the Philadelphia College of Pharmacy. Here he specialised in the production and marketing of drugs. He graduated in 1874 and became a travelling salesman for a large New York pharmaceutical firm. Two years later he joined another pharmaceutical firm which had developed gelatine-coated tablets. He shone, and was given the chance to travel to far-flung regions of the world to collect raw materials that might be used in medicines. He also looked for new sources of cinchona bark, the source of quinine used for the treatment of malaria.

Henry was hard-working, ambitious, and intelligent with the perfect manner for a salesman. At the age of only twenty-six, he was establishing a name for himself, publishing articles in several pharmaceutical journals. It was at this time that he resumed contact with his old classmate Silas Burroughs. This was a correspondence that was to change Henry's life. In 1879 Silas Burroughs asked Wellcome to join him in London.

The technique of compressing medicine into tablets had been developed in America, the advantage being that it was safer because it was easier to give a standardised dose. Back in Britain the traditional method of making medicines with a pestle and mortar was still used. Burroughs worked for the drug firm John Wyeth and Brother, being their sole agent in London. He decided to ask Wellcome to become a partner in a firm importing the compressed tablets and selling them in Britain and Europe. Henry saw the potential and 'Burroughs and Wellcome' began trading in 1880. Soon they realised the potential of manufacturing these 'tabloids' themselves. They opened a factory in London.

The tabloids were a great success. In the late 1880s Burroughs and Wellcome pioneered the development of a new machine able to produce six hundred a minute, all containing a uniform amount of the active product.

Burroughs and Wellcome placed great emphasis on the welfare of their workers. When their factory in Dartford was built, the employees worked an eight hour day, allowing time for learning and recreation. 'Acacia Hall' was built which was equipped with sports facilities and a library. The entertainments committee organised outings to the seaside and literary and musical events.

Burroughs died in 1895 of pneumonia. The men were of very different character and there had been much discord and falling out over the years. Indeed the partnership was in the process of being renegotiated at the time of Burroughs' death. Wellcome was left with full control of the business. He expanded it and opened branches all over the world so that it became the leading company in the British pharmaceutical industry.

The success of Burroughs Wellcome and Co. was due to novel methods of publicity.

Sales depended on travelling salesmen who visited doctors face-to-face. They advertised in medical journals. Chests containing their products were presented to notable people, including explorers and missionaries, royalty, and prime ministers. They held banquets and exhibited at trade shows and medical meetings. Whilst we may be used to these methods today, they were revolutionary at the time.

Another important innovation was the setting up of the Physiological and Chemical Research Laboratories in 1894. This was in response to the need to produce an effective and safe anti-toxin serum against diphtheria, the production of which had been pioneered in Berlin and Paris. The company were committed to scientific advancement rather than commercial success and the scientists employed were allowed the freedom to publish in scientific journals. Some of the best scientists in the country came to work there.

As well as the successful production of diphtheria anti-toxin, the Wellcome Research Laboratories have made many important breakthroughs. These include the isolation of histamine, leading to the manufacture of antihistamines. They were the first in Britain to produce insulin and also developed methods of standardising it, so making it safer.

The success is reflected in the share of five Nobel Prizes by Wellcome scientists. Henry Wellcome was elected a Fellow of the Royal Society in 1932 in recognition of his services in the promotion of scientific research.

In 1901 Wellcome married Syrie Barnardo, daughter of Doctor Thomas Barnardo, founder of the orphanages that bear his name. It was not a happy marriage. In particular, she did not like the extensive travel that Henry undertook. She was twenty-six years younger than he was. They had one son, Henry Mounteney. Syrie had an affair with Somerset Maugham, and following an acrimonious divorce, the marriage ended in 1916. Syrie became one of the first interior designers, and her clients included Wallis Simpson and Noel Coward. She died in 1955. Mounteney, who struggled at school, probably suffering from dyslexia, became a farmer in Buckinghamshire.

Henry's endeavours to promote the business made him a London socialite. He took a house in a fashionable part of London and hosted all sorts of entertainment. His friends included members of the theatrical world such as Oscar Wilde, explorers such as Henry Morton Stanley, and scientists such as Joseph Lister. But this glamorous life hid an inner loneliness and apart from his friend Stanley, nobody really became close.

Wellcome had a variety of interests as well as the pharmaceutical business, and in 1924 he incorporated them all into the Wellcome Foundation Ltd, of which he was sole shareholder and governing director.

He developed an interest in tropical medicine. On travels abroad, he was deeply affected by the poor conditions and the diseases rife in Africa and South America. In Khartoum he donated equipment to the planned Gordon Memorial College, which became the home of the Wellcome Tropical Research Laboratories in 1902. It was able by public health measures to reduce the incidence of malaria by 90 per cent.

Wellcome even funded a floating laboratory allowing researchers to reach far-flung reaches of the Nile.

He founded the Wellcome Bureau of Scientific Research in 1913 to oversee the Chemical and Physiological Research Laboratories as well as research into tropical medicine. To aid research into tropical medicine a museum of images, specimens, and artefacts was founded in London. It has been brought up to date and is now a distance learning facility for workers in developing countries. The Wellcome Trust still supports many research projects throughout the world.

Wellcome was a great collector of objects connected to the history of medicine from ancient days to the present. He also had an interest in anthropology and archaeology, and indeed his collecting got rather out of control. It even included twelve stuffed crocodiles. At the time of his death he had collected some 1.5 million objects and books. (In 1930 his collection was five times larger than that of the Louvre.) He organised archaeological digs. He held exhibitions and created a Historical Medical Museum aimed to be of use to the medical profession. In 1932 his library and two museums as well as two of his research laboratories moved into a newly acquired building in the Euston Road, now called the Wellcome Building. The bulk of the museum collection was moved to the Science Museum in the 1970s.

With increasing age came increasing loneliness. He had become bitter and reclusive and lost his sparkle. His son had no interest in the business, so Henry gave a lot of time during the last few years of his life to organising his affairs to ensure his good work carried on after his death. He vested the entire share capital of his company to the Wellcome Trust. Wise investment by the trustees and merger with other pharmaceutical companies has led to enormous growth of the Wellcome Trust, so much so that in 1995 the trust's assets were £6.8 billion. In 2007 £650 million was spent on research. This would have pleased Wellcome whose wish was to improve mankind's wellbeing through scientific enquiry and also to promote the study of the history of medicine.

Wellcome's health had been poor for some time. It seems he had suffered from ulcerative colitis for years. Finally, with advanced bladder cancer, he died from pneumonia on 25 July 1936 in the London Clinic. He was eighty-two. His ashes were interred in the churchyard of St Paul's Cathedral and there is a plaque commemorating him in the crypt of St Paul's next to one for Alexander Fleming.

He had been knighted in 1932 and made an honorary Fellow of the Royal College of Surgeons.

Daniel K. Ludwig (1897–1992)

The Ludwig Institute for Cancer Research, part of the Nuffield Department of Medicine in the Old Road Campus Research Building, is named after the business magnate and philanthropist Daniel K. Ludwig.

Ludwig was born on 24 June 1897 in Michigan, USA. At the age of nine he began earning money by selling popcorn and shining shoes. At nineteen he borrowed $5,000 to purchase and repair an old paddle steamer and this led over the years into a huge fleet of supertankers. His many other business interests included the oil and gas industry, coal and mineral mining, and a chain of luxury hotels. One project, however, was a failure. He purchased a large area of jungle in Brazil with the aim of deforesting and replanting it with Burmese trees that would meet the world's need for fibre. He met opposition from conservationists, and despite costs of some billion dollars, the project had to be abandoned.

He founded the Ludwig Institute for Cancer Research in 1971, bequeathing a substantial portion of his estate for the endowment of the Institute. His aims, about which he felt strongly, were to bring the best possible resources and the best minds from all over the world together to conquer the disease. He wanted to ensure that the fruits of research were put into practice. He felt there was the need for an international attack on the disease, and that victory would only come from intense and unremitting scientific research over many decades. In order to accomplish this, there had to be secure and continuing financial support so that funding was not dependent on political whim nor on the vagaries of public interest. The Institute is the largest international non-profit making institute dedicated to understanding and controlling cancer, with nine branches in seven countries.

In Oxford, research includes work on 'combination therapy' to treat cancer including melanoma. It was found that triple therapy involving the use of two 'activating agents' in combination with the drug vemurafinib is effective at killing melanoma cells in culture and shrinking tumours in mice. The work is done in conjunction with Ludwig researchers in Melbourne and Baltimore. It is the stable, long-term funding that has allowed the basic research leading to these advances.

At the time of his death, Ludwig's assets were believed to be of the order of $1.2 billion. For a man of such wealth, many of his tastes were modest. He wore the same plastic raincoat for years and usually flew economy class. For recreation he liked to watch old films starring his friend Clark Gable. He was by nature a conservative, including Richard M. Nixon and Ronald Reagan among his friends.

Ludwig was married to Gladys for nine years, divorcing her in 1937 and marrying again the same year. He died of heart failure in Manhattan on 27 August 1992. He was ninety-five.

Doctor Louis Harold Gray (1905–1965)

The Gray Institute for Radiation Oncology and Biology in the Old Road Research Building is named after Louis (Hal) Gray, physicist and radiobiologist. He is seen as the father of radiobiology and did important work on the effect of oxygenation on the sensitivity of tumour tissue to radiation.

Hal was born on 10 November 1905 in London, the only child of Harry and Amy Gray. He learned practical skills from his mother and helped her do up the house, as money was tight. He loved carpentry. His father, who had a somewhat precarious job as a labourer, was interested in mathematical problems, and he and Hal would go for long walks on Sunday mornings during which Harry would ask his son mathematical problems.

Hal won a scholarship to Christ's Hospital School in 1919 at the age of thirteen. He was really only interested in maths and science and was particularly influenced by one master who held a 'philosophy society' where matters scientific were discussed. One holiday this master took some of the boys to a cancer hospital, perhaps sowing the seed of Hal's future career.

Hal won an exhibition to Trinity College, Cambridge where he obtained a first in Natural Sciences in 1927. He had been made Senior Scholar. For the next three years he was delighted to be a research student working in the prestigious Cavendish Laboratory in

Cambridge, headed by Gray's hero Ernest Rutherford. It was an exciting time in the field of nuclear physics. During this time he published his first paper, 'The Absorption of Penetrating Radiation'. He set about trying to measure cosmic radiation, which led to the formulation of the Bragg–Gray Principle in 1936. (William Lawrence Bragg was Nobel prizewinner and Rutherford's successor). Hal gained his PhD in 1930, the subject of which was the absorption of hard gamma rays. He was a fellow of Trinity College from 1930 to 1934.

Hal has the honour of having a scientific unit named after him, the SI unit of absorbed dose of radiation. The gray (Gy) is the dose of energy absorbed by a homogeneously distributed material with a mass of 1 kilogram when exposed to ionising radiation bearing 1 joule of energy. 1 Gy = 1 J/kg.

Gray was becoming interested in the application of physics to disease in humans. He was influenced by his wife Freye whom he had married in 1932. She had been blind since early childhood. She gained a degree from Cambridge and was a keen Methodist. Later both she and Hal became lay-preachers. It was the time of the Depression and they developed a strong social conscience, for example doing up a cottage to house a family who lived in a squalid caravan.

He took up the post of Physicist at Mount Vernon Hospital in Northwood in London in 1933. His research work was supported by the British Empire Cancer Campaign (BECC, now part of Cancer Research UK). He was also the Prophit Scholar of the Royal College of Surgeons. At Mount Vernon, he set about learning about cancer by going on ward rounds and reading about biology. He built a neutron generator in the grounds from 1937 to 1939.

With the coming of war, Hal was too old to be called up, although his beliefs would have precluded his fighting anyway. He was a member of the Fellowship of Reconciliation.

During the war, great technological advances had been made in the field of nuclear physics, but not for peaceful means. After the war, the Medical Research Council wanted to promote radiobiology and nuclear medicine so that humankind would benefit from this knowledge. In 1946 Gray accepted the post of Senior Physicist then Deputy Director of the MRC's Radiotherapeutic Research Unit at the Hammersmith Hospital in London. Here he supervised the building of a powerful medical cyclotron, allowing him to continue his studies on the biological effects of radiation. He founded the Hospital Physicists Association.

Sadly, disagreements with the Director meant he had to leave the Hammersmith in 1953. However, seeing Gray's potential, fellow scientists saw to it that, with a grant from the BECC and a large anonymous donation, the BECC Research Unit in Radiobiology was set up with Gray at its helm at Mount Vernon Hospital. It was named the Gray Laboratory in 1970, after his death. Gray became its director and was made a Nuffield Fellow. He took a major part in designing the new unit—and was mercilessly teased because, though a prodigious tea drinker himself, he forgot to include a kitchen!

Gray and others published an important paper in the *British Journal of Radiology* in December 1953 entitled 'The Concentrations of Oxygen Dissolved in Tissues at the Time of Irradiation as a Factor in Radiotherapy'. While they were not the first to suggest the possible efficacy of oxygen in radiotherapy, it was this paper that caused excitement among clinicians. In it they showed that oxygen sensitised tumour tissue more than normal tissue, leading to attempts to irradiate tumours under increased oxygen tension.

Gray's outstanding scientific work was recognised when he was elected Fellow of the Royal Society in 1961. He served on many committees, lectured all over the world, and was given many awards. In an age of increasing specialisation, he saw the importance of breadth of knowledge which could itself lead to the birth of new disciplines.

In 1962, as President of the International Congress for Radiation Research, Hal was responsible for organising their meeting in Harrogate in Yorkshire. This involved a great deal of work on top of his usual commitments and he was soon exhausted. This may have contributed to a severe stroke in January 1963 which led to him being off work for five months. Sadly, for one who loved cabinet-making, he never regained use of his left hand. He showed great courage but work was a struggle and he began to doubt his abilities and the future of the unit.

Hal was respected all over the world for his knowledge and scientific understanding, but also for his concern for human beings. He was a family man too. His wife's family had connections with the Channel Isles and Hal and Freye and the children went there every summer for their holidays. The locals loved him for his warmth and simplicity. He was always interested in people and a loyal friend. He is remembered for his infectious laughter.

He had a second stroke and died on 9 July 1965 at the age of only fifty-nine. His ashes were interred in the family vault of his wife's ancestors on Alderney.

Sir Richard Doll (1912–2005)

The Richard Doll Building on the Old Road Campus at the Churchill Hospital is the epidemiology centre in Oxford. It houses the Cancer Epidemiology Unit founded by Sir Richard Doll as well as the Perinatal Epidemiology Unit and the Clinical Trials Service Unit. Sir Richard was Regius Professor of Medicine in Oxford from 1969 until 1979. He is remembered as one of the foremost epidemiologists of all time, who established the association between smoking and lung cancer. In Oxford he is remembered too for his role in founding Green College (now Green Templeton College).

William Richard Shaboe Doll was born in Middlesex on 28 October 1912. His father, who was a doctor, suffered from multiple sclerosis. His mother was a concert pianist, and due to her busy life, he was largely brought up by his grandmother. Richard attended Westminster School where he turned out to be intelligent and athletic, a good cricket player and excellent at mathematics. His was a privileged life, despite the great poverty and social unrest of the time. He had a flirtation with evangelical religion, but this was soon replaced by politics. He joined the Young Communist League and saw it as a means to fight social injustice.

Initially he planned to read mathematics at Caius College, Cambridge. However, disaster followed in his entrance examination after a night spent imbibing the local ale with ex-Westminster students at Trinity. It meant he was offered an exhibition, rather than the scholarship he was aiming for. He was so incensed that he decided to read medicine at St Thomas's instead. Later he was to say that that beer was 'the best drink I ever had' because of the way in which it changed the direction of his life. (It is interesting to ponder whether he might have become one of the Cambridge spies had he entered the university.)

At St Thomas's he joined the Communist Party. He was appalled by the poor living condition of many of the patients, and indeed became a supporter of a free, universal health service. He developed a hatred of fascism and visited both Nazi Germany and the Soviet Union whilst a student. He campaigned for the International Brigade during the Spanish Civil War. Closer to home, he tended the wounds of the men on the Jarrow Hunger March of 1936 when some two hundred men from the north marched to London to protest against unemployment and the poor social conditions of the time.

Sir Richard qualified in 1937 and did his house jobs at St Thomas's before working at the Hammersmith Hospital. He volunteered for the Royal Army Medical Corps. He was involved in the evacuation from Dunkirk in 1940. He then spent time in Cyprus, Greece, and Egypt before working on a hospital ship in the Mediterranean. Whilst in the Middle East he became friendly with Archie Cochrane (see section on John Radcliffe Hospital). He had a lucky escape when one evening he went out with a bomb disposal officer to see what he did. On returning, Sir Richard found his room and car had both been flattened. He was mentioned in dispatches but had to come back to Britain early because he developed tuberculosis of the kidney. He had the kidney removed and made a full recovery.

After the war, his career was somewhat limited because of his known communist sympathies. He began to seek his future in public health and mathematics.

Whilst still a student, Doll had met Joan Faulkner at a Communist Party meeting. She was a doctor and worked at the Medical Research Council and indeed rose to become its Chief Administrator. She was married, but they fell in love and became engaged on VE Day. They married in 1948. It was a long and very happy union, Joan providing him with the support he needed in every aspect of his life. Sadly, they were unable to have children so they adopted a baby boy and girl. Being atheists, they felt there was a place for an adoption organisation that was not affiliated to the Church, so they founded the Agnostic Adoption Society, which they largely funded themselves. They remained passionately interested in politics. In 1951 they co-founded the Medical Association for the Prevention of War. They resigned from the Communist Party in 1957 following the Soviet invasion of Hungary.

Through Joan Faulkner, in 1946 Richard joined a gastroenterology research project on peptic ulcers with Francis Avery Jones at the Central Middlesex Hospital. Whilst there, he attended a statistics course run by Austin Bradford Hill, a move that was to change his life as well as that of many thousands of people. In 1948 Hill, who was trained as an economist, was Reader in Epidemiology and Statistics at the MRC's statistical research unit based at the London School of Hygiene and Tropical Medicine. In 1948 he offered Doll a job there. The two men together were responsible for the development of the science of epidemiology, particularly the study of the causes of non-infectious disease.

They worked well together and their most important work was their study on the cause of lung cancer. In the late 1940s, lung cancer was responsible for thirteen thousand deaths a year in the UK, and significantly this was greater than the number dying from tuberculosis. This epidemic of lung cancer led to various theories, some believing atmospheric pollution was responsible, some tar on the roads, and some smoking. At the time, 80 per cent of men smoked and 40 per cent of women.

Hill and Doll started a retrospective study in 1948 at the request of the Medical Research Council. Twenty London hospitals were contacted and information about patients admitted to the hospital diagnosed with cancer of the lung, stomach, colon, and rectum obtained. Lady almoners interviewed these patients as well as a 'non-cancer control group'. It was a detailed and wide-ranging set of questions covering all aspects of life-style and environment, including of course smoking habits. It soon emerged that there was a real association between smoking and lung cancer, and Doll and Hill published an important article in the *British Medical Journal* in September 1950. They concluded that smoking was 'a factor, and an important factor, in the production of carcinoma of the lung'. However, the paper did not cause the interest that it should have done and many doctors and scientists, most of whom smoked themselves, did not accept the findings.

Hill and Doll saw the need to carry out a long-term prospective study on smoking and lung cancer. They made an inspired choice: they decided to perform the study on members of the medical profession. This was good for a number of reasons. Firstly, it would be easy to follow them up over the years as their address would be recorded on the medical register. Secondly, as doctors usually received good medical care, the cause of their death would be accurately reported. Finally, doctors would be likely to answer the questionnaire accurately. The short questionnaire was sent to the nearly sixty thousand doctors in Britain in October 1951, with help of the British Medical Association. There was a huge response, so much so that the Post Office had to open a sorting office at the London School of Tropical Hygiene and Medicine. The twenty-four thousand male doctors over thirty-five were chosen for the study.

In 1954 Hill and Doll published their preliminary findings in the *British Medical Journal*. They demonstrated a significantly increased incidence of lung cancer in the group of smokers and that the incidence increased with the amount smoked.

In 1956 they demonstrated increased death rates from other conditions including chronic lung disease and heart disease in smokers. This time the study caused great controversy, not least from the tobacco industry and from the government, as over 14 per cent of its tax revenue came from duty on tobacco. Large numbers of doctors gave up smoking. However, the Ministry of Health declined to take action.

By the time of their ten-year report in 1964, Hill and Doll showed that as well as smoking increasing mortality from lung cancer, there was a steady decrease in mortality once smoking stopped. At this stage, the British Medical Association was spurred into action and called for education about the dangers of smoking and legislation including controls on advertising. Sir Richard was very loath to lobby and campaign himself, seeing himself very much as the scientist producing the facts.

The *BMJ* published the fifty-year follow-up in June 2004. The evidence showed that those long-term smokers born between 1900 and 1930 died an average of ten years before similar non-smokers. Encouragingly, stopping smoking significantly reduced the risk of this premature death. On his ninety-second birthday in October 2004 Doll and Richard Peto gave a lecture at the John Radcliffe Hospital on the fifty-year study. The project was wound up later in 2004.

The British Doctors Study was a remarkable piece of research, not least because of the long period over which it was conducted. It was always meticulous, carried out to the highest standards of statistical accuracy thanks to the abilities of Hill, Doll, and Peto. Doll lived long enough to see a marked reduction in smoking, although this was a long and tortuous course with battles to encourage the government to ban tobacco advertising and increase tax on cigarettes. Later Doll came to hope that the combination of the genetic and the environmental approach would lead to winning the war against cancer. He believed that cancer arose from a combination of 'nurture, nature, and luck'.

While we do not have space to consider it here, Sir Richard worked on many other diseases. These include industrial lung disease, in particular asbestosis, the effects of ionising radiation, the safety of oral contraceptives, asthma, and many other conditions. Often the results were controversial and he was called on to present unfavourable evidence. His great intellect and clear thinking made him a formidable expert witness. In addition, his writing was always careful, clear, and incisive. Doll was director of the MRC's Statistical Research Unit from 1961 to 1969. In 1966 he began to work with statistician Richard Peto, who became his protege. This proved to be a hugely fruitful partnership, the two men passionately sharing the goal of preventing premature death and suffering.

In 1969 Doll was appointed Regius Professor of Medicine in Oxford, following on from Sir George Pickering (see section on John Radcliffe

Hospital). The appointment was somewhat controversial, some staff thinking Doll was not a 'proper' doctor. He and Joan lived at Osler's old home, 13 Norham Gardens in North Oxford, which Osler had left for the use of the Regius Professors.

He saw that an important part of his job was improvement and expansion of the medical school. He hoped that promoting excellence in the preclinical school would produce clinical students wanting to go into teaching and research. He worked with Rosemary Rue (see later), the senior administrative officer of the Oxford Region, and this combination of an academic and a National Health Service figure with access to funding was a powerful one. Funding was obtained for five new academic chairs, including one in Social Medicine, supported by the Nuffield Provincial Hospitals Trust. The reputation of the medical school grew so that it became the leading institution in the country, attracting money into the university. Leading scientists were attracted from all over the world. Although respected, Doll was never completely accepted by some of the medical profession in Oxford. He continued his epidemiological research, bringing some of his MRC staff with him to Oxford.

His greatest legacy in Oxford, however, was the founding of Green College (now Green Templeton College), the college for clinical medical students. As early as 1970, Doll and Beeson (the Nuffield Professor of Medicine—see section on the John Radcliffe Hospital) were beginning to think about such a college. Some felt that clinical students were not catered for very well by the university, and indeed they did have different needs from other students. The idea was to found a college that would cater for them, particularly important as there were plans to increase their number, with the aim to reach a hundred clinical students a year by 1977. A college would also create fellowships for clinical staff.

The Observatory site next to the Radcliffe Infirmary seemed the obvious choice. The Observatory building was already the home of Osler House, the students' club. Medical students were consulted in 1976 and the majority of the few who responded to the questionnaire were in favour. There was, however, strong opposition from a few of the consultants in Oxford who felt strongly that the essence of the university was the college system which catered for students in every subject. They did not approve of a college dedicated to one subject. However, legislation was approved by Congregation early in 1977.

The question now was funding. Through Beeson, now back in America, one Doctor Cecil Green, director of Texas Instruments, was contacted and he and his wife visited Oxford in April 1977. Green had been born in England in 1900 but moved to Canada when he was two. Trained as a scientist, he was involved in oil exploration. His vast wealth had been put to good use financing academic posts in America, and he was attracted to the idea of founding an Oxford college. A million pounds was proffered with the stipulation that things moved ahead quickly. The Dolls and Cecil and Ida Green got on very well together which was very beneficial to both parties. Green College opened in September 1979 and Sir Richard was appointed the first warden, following his retirement as Regius Professor of Medicine that year.

However, there was vehement opposition from the medical students. They felt the whole business had been rushed through with no consultation with the student body. One worry was the fact that Osler House, the students' mess, would be located next to the Radcliffe Infirmary, whilst students would be based largely in Headington at the John Radcliffe Hospital. After great and complex manoeuvrings, Green College purchased the old administrator's house on the John Radcliffe site. It was named Osler House, and became the independent university club catering for social and sporting needs of all clinical students, independent of Green College. To Sir Richard's sadness, only a very small number of students elected to join Green College in its first year, the vast majority staying with their old college. Partly for this reason and partly because of a genuine interest in the applied social sciences, the decision was made to admit students of these subjects.

Richard and Joan were totally dedicated to Green College. Joan took a practical interest and personally visited factories to get furnishings at budget prices. Richard spent evenings in the college bar, getting to know students and fellows.

The College was officially opened by the Chancellor of the

University, Sir Harold Macmillan, on 13 June 1981. By now it was increasing in numbers and popularity so that it came to be an important part of medical education in Oxford. It wouldn't have happened without the Dolls, and they were very proud of this achievement. They had made a large financial contribution over the years too, for example giving fees from lectures and honoraria to the college. Sir Richard retired from being warden in 1993.

Sir Richard received a multitude of awards and honours in his long life. He was elected to the Royal Society in 1966, knighted in 1971, and made a Companion of Honour in 1996.

Sir Richard was a complex character. He had undoubted qualities of leadership and a definite quiet presence which could be intimidating at times. Some never found him easy to converse and deal with, although students of Green College recall his kindness and ability to show an interest in them. Work was his all-consuming passion, and he was efficient and never wasted a moment. His aim in life was to be a 'valuable member of society'. One anecdote illustrates a human side: he brought a kitten that he had rescued in France back with him via Dunkirk, tucked inside his uniform. When he had to give it up on returning to England, he described it as 'one of the saddest moments of my life'.

Joan died in 2001 and Richard was bereft. But he rallied and soon looked after himself as well as working in his office in Green College every day. He continued to travel abroad, lecturing and taking part in collaborative research even in his last year. He believed the elderly should live life to the full and even went on a camel ride in the Arabian desert.

The epidemiology unit moved into the Richard Doll Building on the Headington Campus in June 2005 but the following month, Sir Richard had a silent myocardial infarction. He died of heart failure in the John Radcliffe Hospital on 24 July 2005, aged ninety-two.

The Richard Doll Building was formally opened in September 2005, and by a strange coincidence, his death certificate arrived there that very same day: he was part of the British Doctors Study! The memorial stone in the Richard Doll Building is inscribed with his own words:

'Death in old age is inevitable but death before old age is not.' This very much sums up his life's work.

Sir John Badenoch (1920–1996)

The Badenoch Building on the Old Road Campus at the Churchill Hospital is named after John Badenoch, consultant physician in Oxford from 1966 until his retirement in 1985. It houses the Research Facilitation for the Medical Science Division.

John was born on 8 March 1920. His family home was in Banffshire in Scotland but his father was a GP in Leyton in Essex. John went up to Oriel College, Oxford in 1938 and then did his clinical training at the Radcliffe Infirmary. This was the time when the clinical course in Oxford was resurrected, partly in order to train students evacuated from the London medical schools. There were some sixty students, under the care of Doctor Alec Cooke.

He won a Rockefeller student fellowship in 1941 and studied at Cornell Medical School in New York. His journey home in 1943 was somewhat eventful during the Battle of the Atlantic. It took him some three months, setting out on several occasions and having to turn back.

In 1944 he became house physician to Professor Leslie Witts at the Radcliffe Infirmary. He was then called up and served as a medical officer in Nigeria and Ghana, before returning home to be in charge of a small military hospital for officers in Kent.

On demobilisation in 1948 John's father had passed away, so John did a short spell in his practice in Essex to help out. Although this was not the career for him, it did influence his way of dealing with patients later in his career.

He returned to Oxford in 1949 as research fellow in Professor Witts' department. He worked with Doctor Sheila Callender on malabsorption, in particular the mechanisms of anaemia in this condition. His work using radio-isotopes and gastric biopsy in clinical investigation was groundbreaking, and he was invited to give the Goulstonian Lecture for the Royal College of Physicians in 1960.

However, he found that his opinion was being sought on clinical problems by GPs and he decided to devote himself to clinical medicine, becoming a National Health Service consultant physician in 1966. Whilst his academic work had been in the field of gastroenterology, he was very much a generalist.

His patients loved him. He could converse with all manner of patient, and always had time for them however busy he was. He combined clinical skills and a scientific approach with the wisdom of a family doctor learned from his father.

He played an important role in teaching medical students. He was Director of Clinical Studies from 1954 to 1965. His interest in medical education led to important work on committees planning the new clinical school at Cambridge, and the planning of the John Radcliffe Hospital.

Badenoch was one of those people able through hard work to accomplish a great deal. He sat on numerous committees on top of his clinical workload. He also played a large part in life at Merton College where he was a fellow and later sub-warden. He was also an examiner for the Royal College of Physicians and chairman of the examining board. As the Hans Sloane Fellow he helped overseas doctors with their postgraduate training.

In 1977 John was invited to give the Lumleian Lecture for the Royal College of Physicians. It was entitled 'The King is Dead: some medical observations on the course of English history'. It is a fascinating look at the illnesses of the Tudors and Stuarts, including Queen Anne and her son the Duke of Gloucester who were attended by John Radcliffe (see section on John Radcliffe Hospital).

Even after retirement, he continued to sit on many committees, including serving on the General Medical Council and the British Heart Foundation. He was knighted in 1984.

He found time for his interests outside medicine, including bird-watching, gardening, and photography. In 1943 he had married Anne Forster and they had two sons and two daughters.

Sir John died on 16 January 1996 aged seventy-five, of a pulmonary embolism. He is buried at the family home in Banffshire.

Doctor Donald Richards (1920–1994)

The New Richards Building on the Old Road Campus at the Churchill Hospital is named after Donald Richards MBE, a leading general practitioner in Oxford.

Donald Hibbert Richards was born in London on 12 March 1920. He was educated at Radley College where he was head boy. He did his medical training at Clare College, Cambridge and St Bartholomew's Hospital in London. His training was, however, protracted by the war and he became a Major in the Royal Army Medical Corps. He worked on returning troopships at the end of the war. He qualified in 1947.

Donald worked in general practice in Oxford from 1951 to 1986. He started in a surgery attached to his house in St Andrew's Road in Old Headington. He then worked at the surgery in Old High Street, Headington, which now bears his name, and the Donnington Health Centre on the Iffley Road.

He was an innovator in Primary Care. One of his main contributions was the setting up of the scheme whereby health visitors and practice nurses were attached to general practice surgeries, something we take for granted today.

He was always keen to establish links between the general practices and the hospitals in Oxford, working with the consultants. With Professor Peter Sleight he piloted a scheme whereby a GP was formally attached to a medical specialty. He also played an important role in establishing the Oxford Postgraduate Medical Centre with Sir George Pickering. He was particularly interested in end of life care and was instrumental in the setting up of Sir Michael Sobell House Hospice. He also pioneered research into depression following hysterectomy.

Donald was very much part of life in Headington where he lived. He was a churchwarden at St Andrew's Church. During his years in practice he came to realise the social and spiritual needs of many in the community. For example, whilst he might visit an elderly patient at home and write a prescription, there might be no-one to take it to the chemist. With the then vicar of St Andrew's, Derek Eastman, he set up a good neighbour scheme called the 'FISH Scheme' to provide support and fellowship for the needy. It was instituted in Headington in 1961, and has since spread to other places. A small stained-glass window in the baptistery of St Andrew's Church commemorates this. In addition to a verse taken from the Book of Revelation there is a river, a reminder of Donald's enjoyment of fly fishing.

In his younger days, Donald was a keen rowing man, winning the Ladies' Plate at Henley with Radley in 1938. Whilst formal 'blues' were not awarded during the war years, Donald rowed for Cambridge in 1941 and again in 1942 as President of the Cambridge University Boat Club.

He retired in 1986 and was awarded the MBE the following year. Donald suffered from emphysema for many years and died in 1994 at the age of seventy-three. He is survived by his wife Peronelle and two sons and two daughters, three of whom are doctors.

The New Richards Building houses the National Perinatal Epidemiology Unit (NPEU), the Childhood Cancer Research Group (CCRG), and the George Centre for Healthcare Innovation. It is fitting that one who contributed so much to medicine in Oxford should be remembered in this way.

Dame Rosemary Rue (1928–2004)

The University Division of Public Health and Primary Health Care at the Old Road Campus near the Churchill Hospital is named after Rosemary Rue. She was a gifted administrator who overcame great misfortune to become one of the most influential medical figures in Oxford and beyond. One of her most important achievements was her work to improve career opportunities for women doctors.

Elsie Rosemary Laurence was born in Essex on 14 June 1928. Her father was an accountant and her mother a musician. The family soon moved to London and Rosemary won a scholarship to Sydenham High School, but with the coming of war and the Blitz, she was evacuated to live with relatives in Devon. Here she developed abdominal and spinal tuberculosis and was bedbound for nearly a year. It was during a long hospital stay that she decided to become a doctor.

She entered the Royal Free Medical School in London in 1945. It was one of the few medical schools to admit women. However, Rosemary married a pilot instructor, Roger Rue, and when she informed the medical school administrators that she wanted to change her surname, she was duly dismissed. She therefore moved to Oxford to continue her training and qualified in 1951, taking the London external examinations.

Her first job was at the Cowley Road Hospital working for geriatrician Lionel Cosin (see earlier). However, when it was discovered that not only was she married but also had a newborn son, she was dismissed by the authorities. She got a post as a general practitioner in East Oxford, her patients being mostly workers from the Cowley motor plant.

It was here that misfortune struck again: she caught poliomyelitis from a patient in 1954. She woke one day with a fever and headache, and soon realised it was polio. Characteristically she finished her day's work. This was a cruel blow as she was believed to be the last case in Oxford and it was only six months before the Salk vaccine became available. One leg was severely affected, so much so that she could not continue as a GP. Even with crutches and callipers she could barely walk, and certainly could not carry a medical bag.

Her marriage having sadly come to an end, she returned to her parents' home in Hertfordshire in despair. She spent the next ten years recuperating, and held a number of posts, at one stage teaching biology and chemistry in a girls' school. Once recovery allowed she took a post as a GP working for a doctor who had lost a leg through sarcoma. They used to joke that between them they had two legs. Her disability made employment difficult. When attending a job interview that required climbing stairs, she would phone to cancel the interview saying she had accepted another post. However, she persisted where many would have given up.

In 1965 she applied for the post of Assistant Senior Medical Officer in the Oxford Regional Hospital Board (ORHB). Thus began a long and fruitful career in hospital administration and public health in the Oxford region. In 1973 she was appointed Regional Medical Officer to the Oxford Regional Health Authority (ORHA) and in 1984 she became Regional General Manager.

Rosemary achieved much both nationally and locally over the years, promoting community medicine and helping modernise the healthcare system. She helped establish the Faculty of Community Health (which later became the Faculty of Public Health). It was an exciting time as the Macmillan government in the 1960s saw the need for building new modern hospitals. Rosemary made sure the Oxford region got its fair share of the money available and new hospitals were built in Reading,

Swindon, and Milton Keynes. In the last case, she was influential in planning the health services for the new town. She realised that all hospitals had the same basic needs such as facilities at the bedside and width of corridor, so with a stroke of genius she developed basic modules that could be used in all new hospitals, so reducing architects' fees.

However, perhaps her greatest legacy is the change she brought about that allowed women doctors to develop their careers in specialist medicine as well as having a family. Having suffered discrimination herself, she saw the need for change. She discovered some hundred and fifty women doctors in the Oxford region who were insufficiently employed. She interviewed them and within a few months had found employment for fifty of them. She did it by setting up a variety of flexible part-time training schemes, working hard to cajole local consultants and the Royal Colleges to support her. It became possible for women doctors to choose to follow any branch of medicine knowing that they would not be at a disadvantage. The women she helped were known as 'Rosemary's babies'. These schemes later spread all over the country. In recognition of her work, she was elected president of the Medical Women's Federation in 1982.

Rosemary combined a quiet determination and shrewd political judgement with a broad knowledge of health services. She was an inspiration to many, widely loved and respected. Small and birdlike, she had great determination and energy, and it was this that allowed her to achieve so much despite her setbacks. This is reflected by the variety of positions she held. Thus after her official retirement in 1988, she was president of the Faculty of Public Health. She was President of the British Medical Association, Professor of Public Health at the London School of Hygiene and Tropical Medicine, and Vice-President of the Alzheimer's Society. She was a founding fellow of Green College in Oxford. She was made a Dame of the British Empire in 1989.

Rosemary lived in her cottage in Stanton St John near Oxford for forty years. Suffering from bowel and breast cancer, she died there on Christmas Eve, 2004 at the age of seventy-six. She was cared for in her last illness by her beloved sons and grandchildren.

Terence and Mathilda Kennedy

The Kennedy Institute of Rheumatology on the Old Road Campus of the Churchill Hospital is named after the philanthropists Terence and Mathilda Kennedy.

They founded the Kennedy Institute of Rheumatology in 1965, with a sum of £500,000. The original institute was housed at the Hammersmith Hospital in London and was the first institute in the world totally dedicated to rheumatology.

In 2010 the Kennedy Institute and the University of Oxford entered into a collaborative agreement to build a new rheumatology research institute in Oxford. The Kennedy Institute works with the Nuffield Department of Orthopaedics, Rheumatology and Musculoskeletal Sciences.

The Kennedy Trust is a registered charity giving financial support for research in rheumatology. It has always been a flagship of the Arthritis Research Campaign UK. Mathilda Kennedy was the daughter of Michael Marks, founder of Marks and Spencer. The trust came into being because she and her husband Terence were full of respect and affection for their GP Doctor Leslie Lankester who was crippled by arthritis. They wanted to help future sufferers of rheumatic diseases. Sadly Mathilda died before their dream could be realised, but the trust has carried on her good work.

Mathilda was a great philanthropist, particularly in the fields of medicine and education. She married Terence Kennedy late in life and did not have any children of her own.

Photographic Credits

John Radcliffe Hospital

Doctor Nicholas Tingewick: Lanercost Priory, courtesy Colin Corlett, Northumberland-Tales.com

Doctor John Radcliffe. After Sir Godfrey Kneller (1712): Oxford University Hospitals

Thomas Rowney: Oxford University Hospitals

The Reverend Doctor Frederick Barnes: Christ Church Archives

Sir Hugh Cairns: Wellcome Library, London

Professor Paul Beeson: Oxfordshire Health Archives

Professor Archibald Cochrane: courtesy of Cardiff University Library, Cochrane Archive, University Hospital Llandough.

Doctor Lionel Cosin and Doctor George Adams: Courtesy of British Geriatrics Society Archive. Reproduced with permission

Doctor Philip Bedford:
    Courtesy of Oxford Mail/The Oxford Times (Newsquest Oxfordshire)

Sister Howells: Courtesy of Oxford Mail/The Oxford Times (Newsquest Oxfordshire)

Miss Anne Anderson: Copyright Royal College of Obstetricians and Gynaecologists. Reproduced with permission

Sir Michael Kadoorie: Courtesy Kadoorie Foundation

Warneford Hospital

The Reverend Doctor Samuel Warneford: Oxfordshire Health Archives

The Reverend Doctor Vaughan Thomas: Oxfordshire Health Archives

Doctor Alexander Neill: Courtesy Headington History

Doctor Robert McInnes: Oxfordshire Health Archives

Miss May Davidson: Courtesy British Psychological Society

Nuffield Orthopaedic Centre

Charles Wingfield: Courtesy Headington History
Mr Robert Gathorne Girdlestone: Courtesy Oxford University Hospitals NHS Trust
William Morris, Viscount Nuffield: the Warden and Fellows of Nuffield College, Oxford
Octav Botnar: Courtesy Camelia Botnar Foundation
Lord and Lady Tebbit: with kind permission

Churchill Hospital

Lady Churchill: Oxfordshire Health Archives
Sir Michael Sobell: Courtesy Sobell Foundation
Doctor Alastair Robb-Smith: Oxfordshire Health Archives
Professor Geoffrey Harris: photograph by Bassano Ltd., copyright National Portrait
    Gallery, London.

Old Road Campus, Churchill Hospital

Sir Henry Wellcome: Courtesy Wellcome Foundation
Doctor Louis Gray: Courtesy Gray Institute
Doctor Donald Richards: Designers/engravers, David Peace and Sally Scott. Courtesy
    Doctor Stephen Richards and Father Darren McFarland
Dame Rosemary Rue: Courtesy of the Editors, Oxford Medical School Gazette

My thanks too to the many other people not mentioned here for their contributions. I
    have done my utmost to obtain permission to reproduce photographs, but if I have
    infringed any copyrights I will gladly correct this in future editions.

Bibliography

John Radcliffe Hospital

Doctor Nicholas Tingewick
V. L. Bullough, 'Medical Study at Medieval Oxford', *Speculum*, vol. 36, no. 4 (1961) 600–12
K. Dewhurst, *Oxford Medicine* (1970)
Dictionary of National Biography
Emden, *A Biographical Register of the University of Oxford to AD1500*
E. B. Fryde and J. R. L. Highfield, *An Oxfordshire Deed of Balliol College* (1955)
C. Hibbert, *The Encyclopaedia of Oxford* (1988)
H. E. Salter and M. D. Lobel, Victoria County History. *A History of the County of Oxford: Volume 3: The University of Oxford* (1954)
Doctor William Harvey
K. J. Franklin, *William Harvey: The Circulation of the Blood* (1958)
T. Wright, *William Harvey: A Life in Circulation* (2013)
C. Zimmer, *Soul Made Flesh* (2004)
Doctor Thomas Willis
P. Allen, 'Medical Education in Seventeenth Century England', *Journal of the History of Medicine and Allied Sciences*, vol. 1 (1946) 115–43
K. Dewhurst, *Oxford Medicine* (1970)
K. Dewhurst, *Thomas Willis's Oxford Lectures* (1980)
K. Dewhurst, *Willis's Oxford Casebook* (1650–52) (1981)
J. T. Hughes, *Thomas Willis 1621-1675: His Life and Work* (2009)
C. Zimmer, *Soul Made Flesh* (2005)
Doctor Richard Lower
R. Lower, *Dr Lower's and Several Other Eminent Physicians Receipts* (published posthumously 1701)
R. Lower and E. King, 'An Account of the Experiment of Transfusion Practised upon a Man in London', *Philosophical Transactions of the Royal Society of London*, vol. 2 (1667) 557–64
C. Zimmer, *Soul Made Flesh* (2005)

Doctor John Radcliffe

A. G. Gibson, *The Radcliffe Infirmary* (1926)

I. Guest, *Dr John Radcliffe and His Trust* (1991)

C. R. Hone, *The Life of Dr John Radcliffe* (1950)

John Radcliffe's Prescription Book, Radcliffe Science Library

John Radcliffe's Report on the Duke of Gloucester, Radcliffe Science Library

A. Moss, *The Radcliffe Infirmary* (2007)

A. H. T. Robb-Smith, *A Short History of the Radcliffe Infirmary* (1970)

Robb-Smith Archive, 13 Norham Gardens, Oxford

A. Sakula, 'Dr John Radcliffe, Court Physician, and the Death of Queen Anne', *Journal of the Royal College of Physicians*, vol. 19, no. 4 (1985), 255–60

Thomas Rowney

A. H. T. Robb-Smith, *A Short History of the Radcliffe Infirmary* (1970)

P. Somerset Fry, *Kings and Queens* (1990)

Third Earl of Lichfield

A. G. Gibson, *The Radcliffe Infirmary* (1926)

I. Guest, *Doctor John Radcliffe and His Trust* (1991)

C. R. Hone, *The Life of Doctor John Radcliffe* (1950)

A. Moss, *The Radcliffe Infirmary* (2007)

A. H. T. Robb-Smith, *A Short History of the Radcliffe Infirmary* (1970)

J. M. Robinson, *The Lee and Dillon Family Tombs at All Saints, Spelsbury, Oxfordshire*

Fourth Duke of Marlborough

I. Guest, *Dr John Radcliffe and His Trust* (1991)

A. H. T. Robb-Smith, *A Short History of the Radcliffe Infirmary* (1970)

Lord Joseph Lister

L. Farmer, *Master Surgeon: A Biography of Joseph Lister* (1962)

J. Lister, *On the Antiseptic Principle of the Practice of Surgery* (1867)

R. Porter, *The Greatest Benefit to Mankind* (1997)

Sir William Osler

M. Bliss, *William Osler: A Life in Medicine* (1999)

D. W. Collison, 'Osler and Tuberculosis in Oxfordshire, 1909–1919. A Model for Great Britain', Submission for American Association for the History of Medicine, William Osler Medal Contest (1985)

H. Cushing, *The Life of Sir William Osler* (1925)

D. M. Levy, 'Centenary of William Osler's 1885 Gulstonian Lectures and Their Place in the History of Bacterial Endocarditis', *Journal of the Royal Society of Medicine*, vol. 78 (1985) 1039–46

E. F. Nation, 'Osler and Tuberculosis', *Chest*, vol. 64 (1973) 84–7

W. Osler, 'The Gulstonian Lectures on Malignant Endocarditis', *British Medical Journal*, vol. 1 (1885) 467–70; 522–6; 577–9

W. Osler, *The Principles and Practice of Medicine* (1906)

W. Osler, 'Chronic Infectious Endocarditis', *Quarterly Journal of Medicine*, vol. 2 (1909) 219–30

F. Parkes Weber, '"Osler's Sign" and Certain Cutaneous Phenomena sometimes Associated with Heart Disease', *Quarterly Journal of Medicine*, vol. 6, no. 23 (1913) 384–90

The Robb-Smith Archive, 13 Norham Gardens

J. W. K. Ward, *William Osler and the Palace in Pall Mall*

Field Marshal Earl Alexander of Tunis

A. H. T. Robb-Smith, *A Short History of the Radcliffe Infirmary* (1970)

P. Somerset Fry, *Kings and Queens* (1990)

Arthur Sanctuary

E. J. R. Burrough, *Unity in Diversity* (1978)

A. H. T. Robb-Smith, *A Short History of the Radcliffe Infirmary* (1970)

Sir Hugh Cairns

H. Cairns, 'Crash Helmets', *British Medical Journal,* 7 September (1946) 322–3

Annotation, 'Penicillin in War Wounds', *Lancet*, vol. 2 (1943) 742–5

G. J. Fraenkel, *Hugh Cairns: First Nuffield Professor of Surgery, University of Oxford* (1991)

G. Jefferson, 'Memories of Hugh Cairns', *Journal of Neurology, Neurosurgery and Psychiatry*, vol. 22 (1959) 155–66

P. H. Schurr, The Twelfth Sir Hugh Cairns Memorial Lecture: The Cairns Tradition (1988)

P. H. Schurr, Facsimiles of Case Histories taken by Sir Hugh Cairns, KBE, MD, FRCS when Assistant Resident Surgeon at the Peter Bent Brigham Hospital, Boston, Mass., 1926–1927

Professor Ritchie Russell

Obituary, *British Medical Journal*, vol. 282 (1981) 78

E. J. R. Burrough, *Unity in Diversity* (1978)

K. Dewhurst, *Oxford Medicine* (1970)

Munk's Roll

A. H. T. Robb-Smith, *A Short History of the Radcliffe Infirmary* (1970)

W. R. Russell, *Poliomyelitis* (1952)

Sir George Pickering

E. J. R. Burrough, *Unity in Diversity* (1978)

H. L'Etang, 'Sir George Pickering', *Cardiology in Practice*, October/November 1990, 19–20

Obituary, *Lancet*, 13 September 1980

Obituary, *Times*, 5 September 1980

J. McMichael and W. S. Peart, 'George White Pickering, 1904–1980', *Biographical Memoirs of Fellows of the Royal Society*, vol. 28 (1982) 431–49

G. W. Pickering, *High Blood Pressure* (1955)

G. W. Pickering, 'Manners Makyth Man' (President's Address), *British Medical Journal,* 20 July 1963, 133–5

G. W. Pickering, *Quest for Excellence in Medical Education* (Nuffield Provincial Hospitals Trust, 1978)

G. W. Pickering, 'Some New Issues in Medical Education', *Oxford Medical School Gazette,* vol. 20, no. 2 (1968) 95–105

G. W. Pickering, *Creative Malady* (1974)

Professor Paul Beeson

R. Rapport, *Physician: The Life of Paul Beeson* (2001)

Obituary, *Independent*, 11 September 2006

Professor Archibald Cochrane

Munk's Roll

Cochrane website

I. Chalmers, *Journal of the Royal Society of Medicine*, vol. 101 (2008) 41–4 (obituary)

Doctor Lionel Cosin
  A. Barton and G. Mulley, 'The History of the Development of Geriatric Medicine in the United Kingdom', *Postgraduate Medical Journal*, vol. 79 (2003) 229–34
  E. J. R. Burrough, *Unity in Diversity* (1978)
  L. Cosin, 'The Place of the Day Hospital in the Geriatric Unit', *The Practitioner*, vol. 172 (1954) 552–9
  Obituary, *Independent*, 13 April 1994
Doctor Sidney Truelove
  S. C. Truelove and P. C. Reynell, *Diseases of the Digestive System* (1963)
Doctor Philip Bedford
  E. J. R. Burrough, *Unity in Diversity* (1978)
  Obituary, *British Medical Journal*, 14 July 1962, 123
Doctor George Adams
  Obituary, *British Medical Journal*, 30 April 2012
  A. Barton and G. Mulley, 'History of the Development of Geriatric Medicine in the United Kingdom', *Postgraduate Medical Journal*, vol. 79 (2003) 229–34
Professor Sir David Weatherall
  D. Weatherall, *Science and the Quiet Art: Medical Research and Patient Care* (1995)
  D. Weatherall, J. Ledingham, and D. Warrell, *The Oxford Textbook of Medicine* (1983)
Doctor Anne Anderson
  Obituary, *British Medical Journal* (Clinical Research Edition), vol. 286 (1983) 1068

The Warneford Hospital

The Reverend Doctor Samuel Warneford
  E. G. C. Beckwith, *The Reverend Dr. Samuel Wilson Warneford, LL.D. (1763-1855)* (1974), private publication
  W. M. Priest, 'The Rev. Samuel Warneford, M.A., LL.D. (1763-1855)', *British Medical Journal*, vol. 3 (1969) 587–90
  V. Thomas, *Christian Philanthropy Exemplified in a Memoir of the Rev. Samuel Wilson Warneford, LL.D. by His Friend and Fellow-Labourer Vaughan Thomas* (1855)
The Reverend Doctor Vaughan Thomas
  A. G. Gibson, *The Radcliffe Infirmary* (1926)
  R. J. Morris, 'Religion and Medicine: the Cholera Pamphlets of Oxford, 1832, 1849 and 1854', *Medical History*, vol. 19 (1975) 256–70
  R. Porter, *The Greatest Benefit to Mankind* (1997)
  B. Stapleton, *Three Oxfordshire Parishes* (1893)
  V. Thomas, *An Account of the Oxford Lunatic Asylum* (1827)
  V. Thomas, *Memorials of the Malignant Cholera in Oxford, 1832* (1835)
Doctor Frederick Wintle
  Oxfordshire Health Archives
  Oxford University Archives
  B. Parry-Jones, *The Warneford Hospital, Oxford, 1826-1976* (1976)

Thomas Allen
    Oxfordshire Health Archives
    B. Parry-Jones, *The Warneford Hospital, Oxford, 1826–1976* (1976)
Doctor Alexander Neill
    B. Parry-Jones, *The Warneford Hospital, Oxford, 1826–1976* (1976)
Robert Gow McInnes
    Obituary, *British Medical Journal*, vol. 295, 28 November 1987, 1425
    Obituary, *Bulletin of the Royal College of Psychiatrists*, vol 12, February 1988, 74–5
Miss May Davidson
    D. Blackman, Obituary, *Bulletin of the British Psychological Society*, vol. 35 (1982)
    175

The Nuffield Orthopaedic Centre

Mrs Hannah Wingfield
    M. J. Harris, *Nuffield Orthopaedic Centre: A Pictorial History* (2011)
William Morris, Viscount Nuffield
    M. Adeney, *Nuffield: A Biography* (1993)
    P. W. S. Andrews and E. Brunner, *The Life of Lord Nuffield* (1955)
    E. Gillbanks, *Lord Nuffield* (1959)
    P. Hull, *Lord Nuffield* (1977)
    J. Leasor, *Wheels to Fortune* (1954)
    F. J. Minns, *Wealth Well-Given* (1994)
    J. W. K. Ward, *William Osler and the Palace in Pall Mall*
Gathorne Robert Girdlestone
    J. Trueta, *Gathorne Robert Girdlestone* (1971)
    M. J. Harris, *Nuffield Orthopaedic Centre: A Pictorial History* (2011)
Lord And Lady Tebbit
    M. J. Harris, *Nuffield Orthopaedic Centre: A Pictorial History* (2011)

The Churchill Hospital

William Drake
    I. Guest, *Doctor John Radcliffe and His Trust* (1991)
Sir William Bagot
    I. Guest, *Doctor John Radcliffe and His Trust* (1991)
Doctor Alastair Robb-Smith
    Epsom College Archives
    Munk's Roll
    A. H. T. Robb-Smith, *A Short History of the Radcliffe Infirmary* (1970)
    T. J. Ryan, 'Behind the Scenes at the Radcliffe Infirmary: 50 years ago', *Oxford Medicine*, February 2007
Doctor John Warin
    Munk's Roll

Professor Geoffrey Harris

    G. Raisman, 'An Urge to Explain the Incomprehensible. Geoffrey Harris and the Discovery of the Neural Control of the Pituitary Gland', *Annual Review of Neuroscience*, vol. 20 (1997) 533–66

    M. Vogt, 'Geoffrey Wingfield Harris, 1913–1971', *Biographical Memoirs of Fellows of the Royal Society*, vol. 18 (1972) 309–29

    G. Weddell, Obituary, *Journal of Anatomy*, vol. 113 (pt. 1) (1972) 151–4

Old Road Campus, Churchill Hospital

Professor Edward Jenner

    R. B. Fisher, *Edward Jenner 1749–1823* (1991)

    www.jennermuseum.com

Sir Henry Wellcome

    R. R. James, *Henry Wellcome* (1994)

    P. Bailey (2009), Wellcome Trust, www.wellcome.ac.uk

Daniel K. Ludwig

    Obituary, *New York Times*, 29 August 1992

Doctor Louis Harold Gray

    Gray Laboratory Cancer Research Trust website www.lhgraytrust.org

    www.rob.ox.ac.uk

    J. F. Louitt and O. C. Scott, *Biographical Memoirs of Fellows of the Royal Society*, vol. 12 (1966), 195–217

    M. Yamasaki, translated by N. Hamada and M. Morimoto, 'The Life of Louis Harold Gray', *Journal of Radiation Research*, vol. 51, January 2010, Supplement

Sir Richard Doll

    R. Doll and A. B. Hill, 'Smoking and Carcinoma of the Lung: Preliminary Report', *British Medical Journal*, vol. 2 (1950) 739–48

    R. Doll and A. B. Hill, 'The Mortality of Doctors in Relation to their Smoking Habits', *British Medical Journal*, vol. 1 (1954), 1451–5

    R. Doll and A. B. Hill, 'Mortality in Relation to Smoking: Ten Years' Observations of British Doctors', *British Medical Journal*, vol. 1 (1964) 1399–1410; 1460–7

    R. Doll, R. Peto, J. Boreham, and I. Sutherland, 'Mortality in Relation to Smoking: 50 Years' Observations on Male British Doctors, Parts 1 and 2', *British Medical Journal*, vol. 328 (2004) 1519–28

    C. Keating, *Smoking Kills. The Revolutionary Life of Richard Doll* (2009)

    R. Peto and V. Beral, 'Sir Richard Doll CH OBE', *Biographical Memoirs of Fellows of the Royal Society*, vol. 56 (2010) 63–83

    J. M. Samet and F. E. Speizer, 'Obituary. Sir Richard Doll, 1912–2005', *American Journal of Epidemiology*, vol. 164, no.1 (2006) 95–100

Sir John Badenoch

    Munks Roll

    Obituary, *British Medical Journal*, vol. 312 (1996) 906

    Obituary, *Independent*, 27 January 1997

    Lumleian Lecture 1977, *Journal of the Royal College of Physicians*, vol. 12, no. 4, July 1978

Dame Rosemary Rue
    Obituary, *Lancet*, 12 February 2005, 566
    Munk's Roll
    Obituary, *British Medical Journal*, vol. 330 (2005) 199
    Obituary, *Guardian*, 12 January 2005
    Royal College of Surgeons, Plarr's Lives of the Fellows

Further reading

John Radcliffe Hospital

General reading:
E. J. R. Burrough, *Unity in Diversity* (1978)
K. Dewhurst, *Oxford Medicine* (1970)
A. G. Gibson, *The Radcliffe Infirmary* (1926)
A. Moss, *The Radcliffe Infirmary* (2007)
R. Porter, *The Greatest Benefit to Mankind* (1997)
A. H. T. Robb-Smith, *A Short History of the Radcliffe Infirmary* (1970)
C. Zimmer, *Soul Made Flesh* (2004)

Sir William Harvey:
K. J. Franklin, *William Harvey: The Circulation of the Blood* (1958)
T. Wright, *William Harvey: A Life in Circulation* (2013)

Doctor Thomas Willis:
K. Dewhurst, *Thomas Willis's Oxford Lectures* (1980)
K. Dewhurst, *Willis's Oxford Casebook (1650–52)* (1981)
J. T. Hughes, *Thomas Willis 1621–1675: His Life and Work* (2009)

Doctor John Radcliffe:
I. Guest, *Doctor John Radcliffe and His Trust* (1991)
C. R. Hone, *The Life of Doctor John Radcliffe* (1950)

Professor Joseph Lister:
L. Farmer, *Master Surgeon: A Biography of Joseph Lister* (1962)

Sir William Osler:
M. Bliss, *William Osler: A Life in Medicine* (1999)
H. Cushing, *The Life of Sir William Osler* (1925)
W. Osler, *The Principles and Practice of Medicine* (1892)

Sir Hugh Cairns:
G. J. Fraenkel, *Hugh Cairns: First Nuffield Professor of Surgery, University of Oxford* (1991)

Professor Ritchie Russell:
W. R. Russell, *Poliomyelitis* (1952)

Sir George Pickering:
G. Pickering, *Creative Malady* (1974)
G. Pickering, *Quest for Excellence in Medical Education* (Nuffield Provincial Hospitals Trust, 1978)

Professor Paul Beeson:
R. Rapport, *Physician: The Life of Paul Beeson* (2001)

Professor Sir David Weatherall:
D. Weatherall, *Science and the Quiet Art: Medical Research and Patient Care* (1995)

The Warneford Hospital

General reading:
E. C. G. Beckwith, *The Reverend Doctor Samuel Wilson Warneford (1763-1855)* (1974)
B. Parry-Jones, *The Warneford Hospital, 1826–1976* (1976)

Nuffield Orthopaedic Centre

General reading:
M. J. Harris, *Nuffield Orthopaedic Centre: A Pictorial History* (2011)

Viscount Nuffield:
M. Adeney, *Nuffield: A Biography* (1993)
P. W. S. Andrews and E. Brunner, *The Life of Lord Nuffield* (1955)
E. Gillbanks, *Lord Nuffield* (1959)
P. Hull, *Lord Nuffield* (1977)
J. Leasor, *Wheels to Fortune* (1954)
F. J. Minns, *Wealth Well-Given* (1994)

Professor Gathorne Girdlestone:
J. Truetra, *Gathorne Robert Girdlestone* (1971)

The Churchill Hospital

Doctor Edward Jenner:
R. B. Fisher, *Edward Jenner 1749–1823* (1991)

Sir Henry Wellcome:
R. R. James, *Henry Wellcome* (1994)

Sir Richard Doll:
C. Keating, *Smoking Kills: The Revolutionary Life of Richard Doll* (2009)
R. Doll, R. Peto, J. Boreham, and I. Sutherland, 'Mortality in Relation to Smoking: 50 Years' Observations on Male British Doctors, Parts 1 and 2', *British Medical Journal*, vol. 328 (2004) 1519–28